D1130957

JIRO IINUMA

Professor Emeritus of Kyoto University

Japanese Farming : Past and Present

NOBUNKYO

Tokyo

First edition 1995

Published by Nosan Gyoson Bunka Kyokai (Nobunkyo), 7-6-1 Akasaka,
Minato-ku, Tokyo 107, Japan. © 1995 by Jiro Iinuma ; all rights reserved.
Printed in Japan.

CONTENTS

CONTENTS

LIST OF FIGURES

iv

LIST OF TABLES

PREFACE

In this book, I intend to clarify the reason why during the past 35 years Japanese agriculture has declined rapidly (for example, the grain self-sufficency ratio declined from 83% in 1960 to 22% in 1993).

The climate of Europe and America is dry in summer, so the harvest does not change very much even when the agricultural labor is extensive or intensive. But the climate of East Asia and Southeast Asia is very humid in summer, so the harvest changes very much whether the agricultural labor is extensive or intensive. Therefore, Japanese agriculture has been developed as an intensive agriculture from ancient times to the present day.

The management of agricultural labor is very difficult, so family or family-like labor has been used, and this has strongly effected many aspects of Japanese society. In this book, I intended to clarify those aspects of Japanese society in Part I, and that of Japanese agriculture in particular in Part II.

Since 1960, the Japanese government made the labor-intensive, small, complex farming system to the labor-extensive, large mono-cultural type, in order to absorb labor which the rapid development of Japanese ecomony required from the agricultural sector. This is the reason why during the past 35 years Japanese agriculture has declined rapidly. If we hope to rejuvenate Japanese agriculture, it is necessary to modernize it based on the labor-intensive, small, complex farming model.

I have made public these discussions in various magazines.

Part I, Chapter 1-10 in *the East* Vol. XXI, No. 1 (1985)-Vol. XXII, No. 1 (1986). The East Publications, Tokyo, Japan.

Part II, Chapter 1 : An entirely new discussion.

Chapter 2 : in *Tools & Tillage* Vol. I. No. 2 (1969), International Secretriat for Research on the History of Agricultural Implements, National Museum, Lyngby, Denmark.

Chapter 3 in *Op. cit.*, Vol. IV, No. 3 (1982)

Chapter 4, "The Introduction of American and European Agricultural Science into Japan in the Meiji Era" in R. T. Shand ed., *Technical Change in Asian Agriculture* (1973), Australian National Univ. Press, Cambera, Australia is combined with "Effects of Industrialization of Agricultural Technology in Japan since 1800, especially after the Meiji Restoration (1868)" in *Acta Museorum Agriculturae* Vol. XI, No. 1 (1976), International Organization of the Museums of Agriculture, Pragae, Czechoslovak.

Chapter 5 in *Japan Quarterly* Vol. XXI, No. 4 (1974), The Asahi Shimbunsha, Tokyo, Japan.

Chapter 6 in *Japan Interpreter* Vol. XI, Autumn (1976), Japan Center for International Exchange, Tokyo, Japan.

Chapter 7 is memorial lecture at 20th Anniversary of Japanese Association of Land Laws, Kyoto, Japan, November 2nd, 1994.

Appendex in *Acta Museorum Agricultuerae* Vol. XVII, No. 1-2 (1983-1984) Pragae, Czechoslovak.

Résumé in *l'espace géographique* n° 2 (1980), Paris, France.

I have revised these articles. The reference books to this book can be found in the bibliography at the end of this book, by author name or published year described in notes in Figures and Tables.

I want to thank the editors of these magazines for the permission to reprint their material in this book, and I wish to thank Mrs. Kazuko Kajiwara and Mrs. Ryoko Uei for reading this book and Mrs. Makiko Hata for giving me support in publishing this book.

Kyoto, Japan, 1995   Jiro Iinuma

Part I

Aspects of Japanese Society

ONE

Prologue : The Origin of Agriculture

I think that each country's society and history has been of decided mainly by its climate. Of course, the same climate has not always created the same society and history. There have been various interactions (or reciprocal effects) between societies that are products of different climates.

There are two general theories of the relationship between climate and history : the static climate theory and the dynamic climate theory. According to the static theory, the same climate always created the same society and history, but the dynamic theory (which I agree with) claims that the same climate did not always create the same society and history.

Climate can be likened to the frame of a painting. We cannot change the size of the frame but we can freely change the painting from a Matisse to a Picasso, Goya, Sodatsu, or Tamayo. Similarly, we cannot change the climate itself, but within its limits we can alter our use of it. For example, until the middle of the nineteenth century there was scarcely any wheat cultivation in the Northwestern United States. But after the Civil War with the opening up of the country by railways and homesteaders, the area rapidly became the most productive wheat belt in the world. The climate hadn't changed.

In this chapter I want to discuss the origin of agriculture. In the first half of this century, the origin of agri-

3

culture was a demanding and attractive subject for scholars worldwide, for example, Vavirov in the Soviet Union, de Candle in Switzerland, Sauer in th United States, and E. Hahn and E. Werth in Germany. Werth's *Digstick, Hoe and Plough* (1954) was the best book produced by these scholars.

Werth understood agriculture as a "culture-complex" composed not only of crops, implements and livestock, but also of all material culture related to agriculture. He thought there was only one orignal area of agriculture in the world, rather than several that spawned independent cultural-complexes.

Werth thought that there were two kinds of agricultural-complexes, the hoe agricultural-complex and the plough agricultural-complex. In the hoe agricultural-complex, taro and yam were the important crops, digsticks and hoes the agricultural implements, and small animals (for example, goats, pigs, hens, and dogs) the livestock. Wheat, barley, the plough, and large livestock such as horses or oxen were noticeably absent.

On the other hand, in the plough agricultural-complex wheat and barley were the main crops, the main implement, and horses, oxen, and other large animals the livestock.

Werth calculates that the hoe agricultural-complex began in Southeast Asia about 15,000 years ago and spread from there to all tropical areas and finally to Central and South America. On the other hand, the plough agricultural-complex seems to have begun in Southwest Asia about 8,000 years ago as a result of the presence of the hoe agricultural-complex. From there it spread to all temperate areas (see Fig. 1).

Hahn maintains that the plough developed from the hoe, whereas Werth believes that it developed from the digstick, and the improved hoe developed from the primitive hoe. He identified six types of hoe in the world — a blade-hole type and five primitive types (Fig. 2).

4

FIG. 1. THE HOE AGRICULTURAL COMPLEX AND THE PLOUGH AGRICULTURAL COMPLEX

E. Werth 1944.

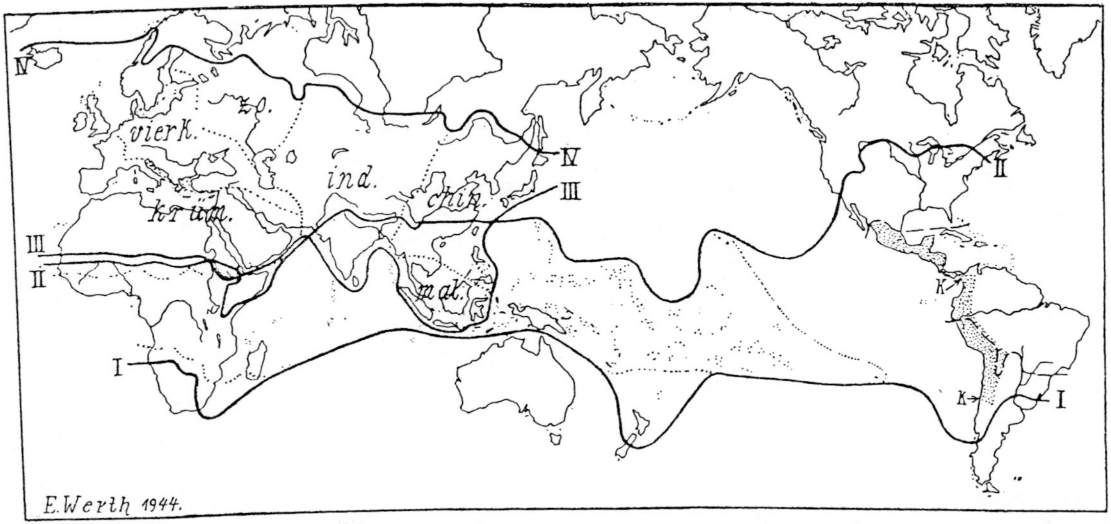

The hoe agricultural-complex is the area between I and II, and the plough agricultural-complex is the area between III and IV.

Source : Werth 1954 ; 18.

5

FIG. 2. SIX KINDS OF HELVES OF HOES

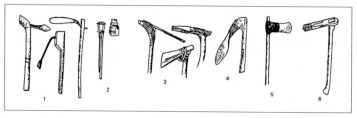

(1) the blade type. (2) the ring type. (3) the bell-hammer type. (4) the bending type. (5) the flag type, (6) the blade-hole type.
Source : Werth 1954 ; 138, 139, 143.

FIG. 3. THE DIFFUSION OF THE BLADE-HOLE-TYPE HOE FROM THE NORTHWEST TO THE SOUTHEAST

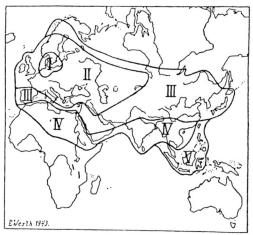

(I) until the Middle Stone Age. (II) until the Neolithic Age. (III) until the Bronze Age. (IV) and (V) the present time.
Source : Werth 1954 ; 95.

The five types of primitive hoe were developed in Southeast Asia and the more advanced type came from the plough agricultural-complex of Northwest Europe.

6

This type of hoe then spead from there to Southeast Asia (Fig. 3).

In Werth's opinion the origin of all cereal cultivation was Southwest Asia. I agree that wheat and barley cultivation can be traced to Southwest Asia but this area cannot also be regarded as the origin of rice culture, because until recently wild rice was not found in the area. Wild rice is, however, easily found in Southeast Asia, making it the likely origin of rice cultivation. Watabe Tadayo claims, following lengthy surveys of Southeast Asia, that the original areas of rice cultivation were Yunnan and Assam, the sources of many large rivers in East and Southeast Asia, for example, the Mecon, Memanu, Pramaptra, and Yangtse. Rice cultivation seems to have spread from Yunnan and Assam to East and Southeast Asia along these rivers.

Studying ancient implements also gives clues to the early development of agriculture. Ishige Naomichi has studied stone-carving knives in ancient East Asia. He concluded that the only stone-carving knives in the world were in China, Korea, and Japan. There were apparently five kinds, the most primitive one coming from old North China and the most advanced from the lower reaches of the Yangtse river. Knives seem to have been first used in North China for cutting ears of millet and to have spread from there down through the regions long the Yangtse River, where they were used for cutting rice. In these regions the knife developed to its most advanced form.

This type of stone knife has been found in burial mounds in both Korea and Southwest Japan, suggesting that rice cultivation spread from the Yangtse River regions by way of South Korea to Southwest Japan. In the earliest stages of rice cultivation in these areas only a hoe and digstick were used. There were no ploughs, proving that rice cultivation in ancient East Asia belonged to the hoe agricultural-complex rather than the plough

7

agricultural-com-plex.

Rice cultivation also spread from Southeast Asia to North China and North India where it came into contact with the existing plough-type agriculture. In both North China and North India rice cultivation led to the development of indigenous ploughs. In this way rice cultivation changed from the hoe agricultural-complex to the plough agricultural-complex.

Werth concludes that during their diffusion around the world the two agricultural-complexes fused to form the present agricultural system.

TWO

The Dry Zone Agriculture and the Humid Zone Agriculture

Generally speaking, ploughs can be divided into two types, those used in dry areas and those used in humid areas. The shape and method of use are, of course, completely different (see Figs. 4).

In dry areas, the plough is used mainly to till shallowly and compress the soil by the sole in order to prevent evaporation from the surface and preserve the water content of the soil. In this case, deep tillage would be harmful because it would encourage evaporation. On the other hand, in humid areas the plough is used mainly to till deeply and to turn the soil over to uproot weeds. Shallow tillage would not kill weeds.

The method of use and shape of the plough in dry areas and humid areas are completely different, and the differences are readily apparent. Broadly speaking, the plough used in dry areas is light and has no moldboard to turn soil over, and that used in humid areas is heavier and has a moldboard. This differentiation is applicable to the situation in Europe and perhaps America, that is, in dry areas the dry-zone plough (D-type plough) is used and in humid areas the humid zone plough (H-type plough) is used. But in Asia the situation is different: the D-type plough is used in both dry and humid areas (apart from the Japanese H-type plough developed in this century). Why?

If one assumes that the plough was intended in a

FIG. 4. MAIN PLOUGHS IN THE WORLD

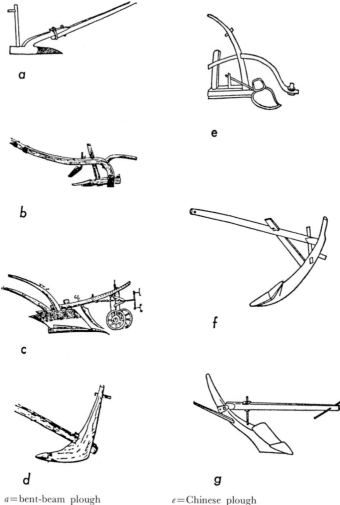

a=bent-beam plough   e=Chinese plough
b=squire plough (primitive) f=no-sole plough (Japanese)
c=squire plough (developed) g=short-sole plough (Japanese)
d=Indian plough
A, d, e are D-type plough, and b, c, f, g are H-type one.
Source : Iinuma 1969 : 291

10

humid area, then one would expect the H-type plough, not the D-type plough, to be used in Asia. But the D-type plough presently used in the humid areas of Asia seems to have been invented in dry areas and to have spread to humid areas. I think this phenomenon is a very important factor in researching the spread of agriculture in Asia.

I have already used the terms dry area and humid area, but now I would like to actually look at the method of differentiation, which falls under the study of climatology. The most commonly used measurement is the index of aridity devised by the French climatologist E. de Martonne.

De Martonne's index is expressed as the formula $I = R/(T+10)$, where I is the index of aridity, R is the collected rainfall in millimeters for a given period, and T is the average temperature in centigrade over the same period. An area that has an index of aridity in excess of 20 during a year period is a humid zone, and an area with an index of less than 20 is a dry zone. If the index is less than 10, the area is classified as desert, and it is impossible to cultivate with rainfall as the sole source of water.

However, even using de Martonne's method of calculation to differentiate between dry and humid zones, the result is not necessarily congruent with the actual style of agriculture. For example, according to the index of aridity, the majority of the northern coast of the Mediterranean has a score of over 20, but the rain falls mostly in winter ; between spring and atumn only one-tenth of the annual total falls. That means it is impossible to grow summer crops planted in the spring and harvested in the autumn. Agriculturally it is closer to the dry zone of Southwest Asia or the south coast of the Mediterranean, which score below 20 on the annual index and therefore would perhaps be better classified with them. Using de Martonne's formula to calculate the index of ardity sum-

11

mer (June — August) in places that score below 5, it is found that it is virtually impossible to grow summer crops. If one then uses the annual index of 20 and the summer index of 5 as a base, it is possible to divide the world into four areas (Table 1) : Area I with an annual index below 20 and a summer index below 5 ; Area II with an annual index above 20 and a summer index below 5 ; Area III with an annual index below 20 and a summer index above 5 ; Area IV with an annual index above 20 and a summer index above 5.

However, it is very difficult to farm with just rainfall in dry areas with an annual index below 20. The main problem is taking advantage of the rainfall, that is, keeping it in the soil for the benefit of the plants. In this regard two musts are to choose plants resistant to dryness (e. g. wheat), and to prevent the evaporation from the surface by frequent shallow tillage, which is generally called "dry farming."

In areas with winter rainfall, where it is impossible to grow summer crops (that is, Areas I and II with a summer index of below 5) in the period from spring to autumn when the land is lying fallow, it is especially beneficial to cultivate the soil shallowly and suppress it by the D-type plough to preserve the water content (this is called "fallow water-conserving agriculture") (see Table 2). Using this water in September or October, it is possible to plant winter crops (mainly wheat). After sprouting, the winter rain can then be relied upon for subsequent growth. Almost all of Area I is desert, and there are few places where dry farming is possible. But Area II has an annual index of over 20 and as it is much more humid and has a more stable water content than Area I, dry farming is possible in most places. Both Areas I and II are, however, classified as dry areas.

Area III like Area I has an annual index of below 20 and is therefore classified as a dry area, but summer rainfall makes the cultivation of summer crops possible,

Table 1. **DIVISION OF GRAIN FARMING IN THE WORLD BY MARTONNE'S INDEX OF ARIDITY**

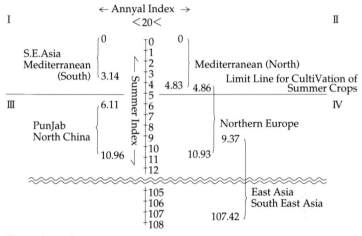

Source : the author

which is a major difference from Area I. In the growing period between spring and autumn, the soil should be turned by a hoe immediately after rain to preserve the water content. In addition, immediately after harvesting and immediately before sowing, the soil should be ploughed using the D-type plough to preserve the water content. (This is called "hoeing water-conserving agriculture,,). In Japan, hoeing is only thought of as a weeding process, and it was only on a trip to India that I learnt the other function of preserving water. In late May in India, the air is burning hot. The day time temperature rises to 40°C. In Japan, however hot the summer, driving in a car with the windows open at least creates a refreshing breeze. But in India in May the breeze is almost unbearably hot. So while driving from New Delhi to Rotack in Punjab State I kept the windows shut.

In the fields on either side of the road there were only

13

a few stacks of wheat straw; there was practically no green in sight. Occasionally there were grazing cattle, but no people. One unusual sight was a field of sugar-cane about forty centimeters high and people working in it.

My destination was the village of Rotieple, about seven miles from Rotack, capital of Punjab, and roughly seventy miles from New Delhi. I got out the car and walked into the field. Again it was a field of sugar cane. Even in the scorching 40°C heat, five or six people were hoeing be-tween the rows. The soil was parched. There were no weeds. They were hoeing simply to preserve the water content.

In the same type III areas, but in places with a high summer rainfall, hoeing serves a double purpose of pre-serving water and killing weeds. Killing weeds has the added advantage of saving the water they would have used.

Finally, Area IV with an annual index of over 20 and a summer index of over 5 is the most humid of the four areas. The cultivation of summer crops is possible, but the rampant weed growth is a problem and weeding be-comes an essential activity. The word "weeding" con-jures up in the Japanese mind the claring of weeds be-tween the rows in the field. But there is another method. The field is rested and at the height of the summer ploughed deeply with an H-type (square) plough. This usually happens twice a summer and kills the weeds by digging them in (this is called "fallow weeding agricul-ture"). In north Europe, for example, it has been com-mon practice since the Middle Ages to grow crops for two years without weeding, and in the third year to leave the field fallow and at the height of the summer to deep plough it twice.

Compared with East and Southeast Asia where techni-ques of repeated hoeing between rows are common, the weeding method of north Europe is obviously much sim-

14

pler. What would result from adopting the simpler method in East and Southeast Asia? Whithout doubt it would be necessary to deep plough fields annually instead of triannually. What are the differences in weed growth between the two areas?

It is hardly necessary to point out the climatic differences. As shown in Table 1, although the summer indexes are both over 5, in north Europe the index is roughly between 5 and 11, but in East and Southeast Asia it ranges from 9 to 107. So there is a major difference in the luxuriousness of weed growth. In Japan in summer, when both the temperature and humidity are high, weeds are so robust that they grow in the cracks in walls. In Japan farming is said to be a constant battle against weeds. It is an example of "hoeing weeding agriculture."

It is not possible, however, to attribute differences in weeds to only climatic differences. Northern Japan has roughly the same climate as Europe, but has far more species of plants. So we must conclude that factors besides climate are responsible for the far greater number of weeds in Japan.

One important factor is the effect of the three ice ages in Europe. Many European plant species were either killed by ice or escaed south, east or west to non-ice areas. After the ice of the last glaciation melted, plants slowly began to return, but some were stopped by the Alps, and others died in the unsuitable dry climate of the Mediterranean. This is the reason an undoubtedly rich plant life in Europe came to be depleted.

The ice age not only killed plant life but also changed the landscape, creating gentle slopes and filling valleys with displaced gravel, sand, and clay. As a result, the soil became far less fertile.

In Europe, in the last half of the nineteenth century there was an area of study devoted to weeds. In Japan, if one excludes the pioneering work of Hanzawa Makoto, who published *Zassōgaku* (Sudy on Weeds) in 1910, then

15

it is not until after the Second World War that the study of weeds was formalized in Japan by Noguchi Yakichi. Why did the study of weeds in Japan lag behind that in Europe, where there are far fewer species? It is possible that the very scarcity of weeds in Europe led to their study there.

Compared with the virulent weeds of East and Southeast Asia, the simplified species of weeds accustomed to the poor environment of northern Europe would obviously be easier to control. From early times in Europe thick sowing has been practiced when growing cereal crops. From the fall of the Roman Empire to the French Revolution, in Europe the production of cereal crops per unit area barely changed. It was 10 bushels of wheat per acre (about 780 kilos per hectare) or less. The ratio in terms of weight of the harvest to seeds planted was a maximum of five to one and a minimum of three one. In north Europe in the Middle Ages the ratio was a maximum of three to one and a minimum of two to one. The northern European harvest reflected thick sowing against weed growth as well as the state of the soil.

According to the results of Kawate Kinzo's research in the Department of Agriculture of Tokyo University, the most efficient method of weed control is to use the basic characteristics of the crops and positively "smother" the weeds. The ideal example of this type of smothering crops is autumn wheat. That is, before planting, the field is ploughed deeply so autumn weeds do not have a chance to grow. And then from the end of March to about April, when spring weeds would normally grow, the wheat is already developed enough to effectively smother their growth. Spring-planted summer crops cannot be used quite as skillfully, but by choosing a "smothering" type it is possible to increase the strength of the plant and achieve similar weed control. It is exactly this method of weed control that has been used for centuries in north Europe.

Table 2. THE TWO TYPES OF GRAIN FARMING

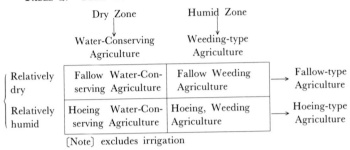

[Note] excludes irrigation

Source : the author

The above-mentioned points are summarized in Table 2. Of course, irrigated areas have been excluded because they drastically change the basic conditions.

In Table 2, the world has been basically divided into dry zones and humid zones, that is "water-conserving agriculture" and "weeding-agriculture." Using fallow and hoeing as points, the world can be redivided into "fallow-type agriculture" and "hoeing-type agriculture."

The plough-agriculture complex, which has a history of nearly 8,000 years, spread first from the dry zone to the humid zone, that is, from "water-conserving agriculture" to "weeding agriculture." The reason is almost certainly that when man began tilling the earth, he first used the more exposed but less fertile plain dry areas, not dense humid forests.

However, the move from agriculture in dry zones (water-conserving agriculture) to that in humid zones (weeding agriculture) can be divided into two processes. One was the process of change from "fallow water-conserving agriculture" to "fallow weeding agriculture" and the other is from "hoe water-conserving agriculture" to 'hoe weeding agriculture.' These two processes have almost separate historical developments. The former could be called the "fallow type agriculture route" (Middle East → south Europe → noth Europe) and the latter

17

the "hoeing-type agriculture route" (North India →
Southeast Asia ; and North China → East Asia). In
fallow-type agriculture, the productivity of the soil is recovered by leaving it fallow, but in hoeing-type agriculture
the soil would be exhausted by leaving it fallow.

The relationship between agriculture in northern India
and in northern China during ancient times is still not
clear. But in India we find the traditional drill, which
resembles the drill found in southern Mesopotamia more
than 5,000 years ago. So we may conclude that agriculture was diffused from southern Mesopotamia to northern
India, and from there to northern China. On the other
hand, the old Chinese drill is said to have originated in
the West. Therefore, northern Chinese agriculture is a
blend of both southern Mesopotamian and northern Indian agriculture.

In hoeing-type agriculture, all crops require hoeing but
in fallow-type agriculture only garden crops (radish, car-
rot, grape, pear, peach, etc.) do. Therefore, in fallow-
type agriculture (as in Europe, for example) the distinc-
tion between agriculture and gardening is very clear.
Agriculture is classified as the cultivation of crops which
do not need hoeing and gardening is the cultivation of
crops that do. But in hoeing-type agriculture the distinc-
tion is not clear. As a result, most agricultural scholars
visiting Japan dismiss Japanese agriculture as "gardening."

In agriculture there is a "law of diminishing return."
When a farmer works on a fixed area of land the return
on the land increases to a certain point, but beyond this
point it begins to decrease.

The point of diminishing return is reached sooner in
fallow-type agriculture than in hoeing-type agricultre.
This is partly due to the modernization of agriculture,
which has increased labor productivity. In fallow-type
agriculture, the saved labor is used to enlarge the area
under cultivation, and therefore, there is no intensification

Fig. 5. THE LAW OF DIMINISHING RETURN IN
FALLOW-TYPE AGRICULTURE AND IN
HOEING-TYPE AGRICULTURE

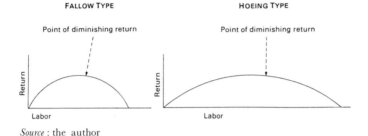

Source : the author

of the work on the same piece of land. In hoeing-type agriculture, however, the area under cultivation tends to remain the same, and the intensity of work increases to the detriment of the crop yield.

The history of the modernization of fallow-type agriculture in, for example, Europe has also been the history of the enlargement of the farmed area because of the development of tools and machines. In hoeing-type agriculture in, for example, Japan, China, and Korea modernization has brought the intensification of labor by hand or tools on the same farmland.

The character of labor in fallow-type agriculture and in hoeing-type agriculture tends to be different. Labor in fallow-type agriculture tends to become extensive, whereas labor in hoeing-type agriculture tends to become intensive. The management of agricultural laborers is intrinsically more difficult than that of industrial workers. On a farm workers are scattered over a wide area, and, moreover, the results of their work only appear after a few months. In addition, the managent of laborers in hoeing-type agriculture is more difficult that in fallow-type agriculture, owing to the different nature of the work as I outlined before. In fallow-type agriculture it is possible to use labores unrelated to a farmer's family but

19

in hoeing-type agriculture the laborers are usually members of the family or household. It follows, therefore, that hoeing-type agiculture encourages a society based on family-style human relations, which tend to last several generations. This is less true of societies based on fallow-type agriculture. Today, for example, the family-style system of human relations between capital and labor is more common in, for example, Japan than in the United States or England.

THREE

Ancient Empires and the Classic Age

THE classic cultures in Greece, China, India, and Israel were established in dry farming areas.

The plough-agricultual complex which began in the mountainous areas of Southwest Asia about 8,000 years ago can be classified as dry farming. As I mentioned before, dry farming is agriculture in areas which have an annual rainfall below 400-500mm, but there can be a variation of up to 200 mm (Fig. 6).

If the annual rainfall is over 600mm then the yield is abundant, but below 300mm there is no crop. Dry farming is, therefore, a very unstable type of agriculture. If irrigation is possible the yield becomes more stable and is increased, possibly as much as two to three times. Therefore, in very early times farmers began diverting small mountain streams in Southwest Asia and using the water for irrigation. Next farmers began diverting larger rivers, for example, the Tigris, Euphrates, Nile, and it became possible to cultivate formerly barren deserts(Fig. 7, 8).

As a result of this more stable and productive irrigation agriculture, about 5000 years ago the first ancient civilization appeared in the lower reaches of the Tigris and Euphrates rivers, rather than in the dry-farming mountainous areas. This first was called Sumer, and there were to be many more city-states built on rivers. Subsequently, these city-states joined together to form one state (Fig. 9),

21

FIG. 6. TWO-FIELD SYSTEM ON THE SOUTH SLOPE OF ELBURZ

Source : the author

FIG. 7. IRRIGATION ON THE SUBURBS OF TEHERAN

Source : the author

FIG. 8. IRRIGATION ON AN OASIS NEAR FROM KWAIT

Source : the author

Fig. 9. BABYLON

Source : the author

the Sumarian Empire, which later developed into the Assyrian Empire and then into the Babylonian Empire. In Sumar a plough had already appeared. It had one plough share and two plough handles, but later evolved to a bended beam plough with just one share and one handle (Fig. 10).

But the construction and maintenance of a large irrigation system using big rivers could not be achieved by just a few people ; it required the social organization of large groups. In addition, the large groups were necessary to defend the crops produced with the irrigation system against attack by nomadic peoples. They also had to defend caravans that traveled great distances to bring stones, metal, wood, etc. unavailable in the desert. Therefore, powerful political control was necessary to organize the concentrated and well-arranged bureaucracy centered on the sovereign powers of either Egypt or Mesopotamia. As it was impossible to farm outside the

FIG. 10. **ANCIENT PLOUGH OF
MESOPOTAMIA**

Source : E. Werth 1954 : 182

irrigation system, the sovereign powers could efficiently control their subjects just by controlling the irrigation system. Karl Marx called this type of society the "general slavery system."

After this, dry farming began in Area II, perhaps having spread from Area I : But as I mentioned before, dry farming was conducted in only a small portion of Area I, while it was conducted throughout Area II.

In dry farming, farmers were more economically and socially independent in small areas in comparison with farmers in the large irrigation agricultural areas. From about the eighth century B. C. in Greece, many small, independent states on clans grew out of the independent dry-farming units, and they developed into the city-states called "polis." The farmers in the small city-states in ancient Greece were more independent than the farmers in the irrigation agricultural areas of ancient Egypt and Mesopotamia. So Greek clans did not need to institute the "general slavery system" of Egypt and Mesopotamia, but instead had a family system of thirty or forty slaves under the strong authority of a patriarch. In ancient Greece the slavery system spread from agriculture to all

26

occupations, and in the fifth century B. C. the brilliant Greek culture flowered on the basis of it.

Of the countries in Area I, Israel has an annual rainfall of about 600mm and so, as in Greece, dry-farming was established by independent small farmers. In both Greece and Israel the annual rainfall is about 600mm, but the summer rainfall is very different. In Greece, it is about 60mm, but in Israel there is virtually no rainfall in summer. It is therefore much harder for the farmers to succeed at dry farming in Isrel than in Greece.

In ancient times Israeli farmers believed that rain was a divine gift. If they obeyed the word of God, then God would be merciful and it would rain, but if they were disobedient it would not rain (Fig. 11). Also, Israel lay between two powerful states, Mesopotamia and Egypt, and the Israelis were always very anxious about their national security. This anxiety confirmed their faith in God. As a result, Judaism was established in the fifth century B. C.

Recently scholars have confirmed that there were also dry-farming city-states in Area III. According to Hou Wai-Lu, the so-called Feng in the Teng Jian system of the Zhou dynasty established in the mid-eleventh century B. C. seem to have been city-states in North China. Conquering clans lived in the Feng and conquered slaves lived around the Feng. In Greek city-states, as I've said, slaves were kept in family units under paternal authority, but in China slaves were not kept as family members but as clans themselves.

The clan system persisted more strongly in the city-states of ancient China than in those of ancient Greece. The relation between Feng in the home country and Feng in th colonies was the same as the relation between the head family and branch families. In this point the clan system clearly remained, illustrating the difference between the hoeing-type agricultural society and the fallow-type agricultural society.

Fig. 11.   JERUSALEM

Source : the author

FIG. 12. CHINESE AGRICULTURAL IMPIEMENTS

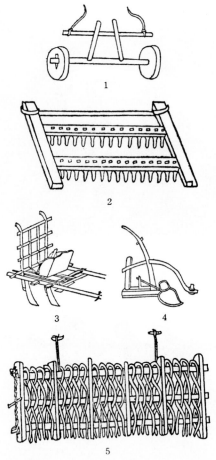

1. roller   2. harrow   3. drill   4. plough
5. leveller
Source : Wang, Vol. 12

FIG. 13.   INDIAN FARMING

(a) Ploughing

(b) Levelling
Source : the author

In ancient China the process of the dissolution of the clan system by the development of agriculture and industry took place from the end of the Chun-Qui period to the Zhan-Guo period, and several city-states combined into a few small states. In the Chun-Qui period many scholars or philosophers, for example, Kong Zi, Meng Zi, Mo Zi, Lie Zi, Lao Zi, and Zhuang Zi, emerged and traveled these states in search of freedom of thought. This led to the flowering of Chinese culture around the fifth to second centuries B. C.

The situation in ancient India is, however, still unclear. It seems that there were sixteen large states in the time of Buddha, and he traveled to these states to teach his religion. According to tradition there were 62 different philosophies and 363 philosophers. The situation of the independent small states seems to have been similar to China in the Chun-Qui period.

In Greece, China, India and Israel the classic cultures flowered in about the fifth century B. C. These cultures were based on the slavery system of dry-farming. I regret being unable to be more specific about India and Israel, but in ancient Greece and China there were many small competing city-states. Many philosophers traveled around these states, bringing about a kind of metaphysical anarchism.

But as I mentioned before, dry farming is not climatically stable. For a more stable political and economic condition, powerful political control over larger areas was necessary. After the classic age, large empires were formed to rule these many small states or city-states : the Han Empire in North China, the Mauria Empire in North India, a few Hellenic states, and later the Roman Empire in the Middle East and Mediterranean region. In the process of establishing these empires the metaphysical anarchy became controlled and institutionalized as a national philosophy or religion. There were ideologies to control all peoples in these great Empires. These ideologies were Confucianism in the Han Empire, Buddhism in Mauria, and Greek philosophy in the Hellenic states and Roman Empire. Today in the modern world many states are the descendants of these ancient empires, and Confucianism, Buddhism, Christianity and Greek philosophy have become classic cultures in their respective countries.

FOUR

The Growth of Feudal Society in Europe

There are many ways to define a feudal society. I define it as a society with both a serf-system and fief-system.

As I described above, the violent variations in the quantity of the harvest in dry zones are not restricted to ancient times and are certainly not rare even in the twentieth century. A friend in Damascus informed me in a letter that the harvest of wheat in all Syria for 1965 was about half the previous year's total, and that the harvest of barley was less than one-third. There are, of course, fluctuations in the quality of the harvest in humid zones, too, but compared with those in dry zones they are quite mild. The problem is that in dry zones, agriculture is being carried out at its extreme limits, that is, the smallest variation in the amount of rainfall can have a more drastic effect than in humid zones.

In dry areas it is very hard to achieve long-term stability with agriculture divided into small units. And if, for example, an irrigation system was planned, powerful political control was necessary to organize its construction and up-keep. In addition, there was the constant danger of invasion, though, on the other hand, total isolation was unfeasible because the community relied for on the outside to supply the materials unavailable in their own dry area (for example, metals, stones, and woods). These circumstances gave rise to the development of central government (Empire). In humid zones, agriculture has

33

from early times been clearly divided into independent areas, which can be gathered from reading, Tacitus' *Germania* or Caesar's *Gallic Wars*. The size of the independent area has decreased with the increase in humidity. That is, in Egypt and Mesopotamia the unified land area was large, in the Greek city-state it was smaller, and in the north of Europe it could only support the smallest family group.

The village community or manors characteristic of northwest Europe in the Middle Ages can't be totally disassociated from this agricultural tradition of small farming units. From this we can conclude that the humid zone agriculture in northwest Europe was responsible for developing on the basis of the independence of family agriculture, the relationship between land and serf.

When Christianity was beginning in southwest Asia, the clan system had already reached its last stages in Germany. Each clan had cleared and settled its own area of the northern European forests, and then developed its own village structure. Each clan not only administered the community land but also maintained peace, kept law and order, and raised troops, that is, it had reached the level of a public way of life. But the system was beginning to change as clans subdivided into families.

Although they were family units, the family head had considerably less power than his equivalent in Greece or Rome. Each member of the family, although respecting paternal authority, had a far stronger sense of independence from superiors or the estate than his ancient predecessors had. Also, under paternal authority were not only blood relatives but also those not connected by blood (according to records they were called servus or famulus, that is, slaves).

But this was different from the slave system of Greece and Rome. From the point of view of social status and financial power they had reached a level of independence. The reason lies, I beleive, in the difference between dry and humid zone agriculture.

It was natural then that as time passed, with discrepancies in levels of production, strong and weak family heads emerged. The relationship between family heads, once equals, slowly changed into ruler and ruled. In addition, certain slaves who owned an allotment of land began to move up the social scale and became more or less equal to the clan members. So out of the remains of the clan system a formal hierarchical system of lords and serfs emerged.

The development of the serf system paralleled the development of the rural community. At the clan level of social development there occurred such primitive practices as forest burning, which is still seen in the most underdeveloped parts of the world. But then came the first influence from Rome — the two-field system (dry zone agriculture) with a biennial rotation, winter crops → fallow (Fig. 14, 15). That was followed by the three-feild system (humid zone agriculture) with a triennial rotation, winter crops → summer crops → fallow. At the same time the cultivation area was divided into three parts for the three-field system.

I'd like to paint a picture of the medieval village. Fig. 16, 17 is a rough plan. Roads pass through the village from three fields. Passing through the dense forest, which forms the border with the next village, one reaches pasture land for cattle and sheep. Walking straight along the road with fallow fields or fields of wheat and barley on both sides, one finally reaches the village center. Facing onto the public square are the lord's fine house and the church. In front of the lord's house is his mill. To use this the villager must pay him in wheat or barley.

Leaving the church and the manor house one comes to rows of ordinary peasant houses. In front of almost every house is a garden in which chickens run freely. In the

FIG. 14. TWO FIELD SYSTEM IN SICILIA

Source : the author

FIG. 15. ROMAN PLOUGH

Source : C. S. Orwin 1949 : plate 3.

back garden are vegetables, apples and pears. The road
divides the village's arable land into three parts. One
area is lying fallow and the other two are planted with
wheat and barley. Each area is again subdivided into
smaller divisions (furlongs). In this furlong the villagers

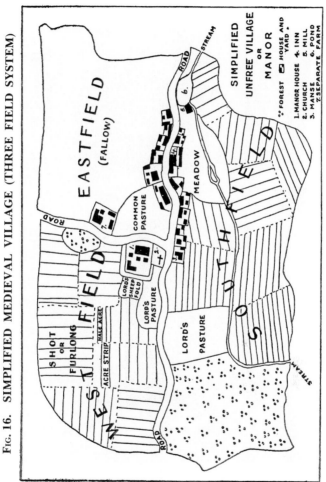

FIG. 16. SIMPLIFIED MEDIEVAL VILLAGE (THREE FIELD SYSTEM)

Source : N. S. B. Gres 1925, 28.

FIG. 17. MEDIAEVAL PLOUGHING (THREE FIELD SYSTEM)

Source : British museum.

work together, one bringing the horse and another the plough etc. to form a ploughing team.

Each furlong of about twelve to twenty acres is again divided into strips of about one acre each. These strips are long and slender to diminish the frequency of plough rotation (compare with the pattern of the fields in the two-field system in southern Europe) (Fig. 18). Each strip was about the right size to be ploughed in a morning. The strip is divided from the next by only a narrow boundary, usually grass or a small stone (Fig. 19). The arable lands held by the lord and the serfs were divided into three equal parts in each of the three fields (if it was not divided this way the three-field system would be impossible). The lands held by each family were spread out and of differing quality and soil type in order that all farmers should have a fair distribution of land size and type.

Between spring and autumn the cows were grazed on the communal pasture. After the harvest, the field of stubble became communal grazing land. (There was surprisingly little permanent pasture land. For example, in a certain English village in 1086, there were only 33 acres of pasture land out of 1,600 acres of farm land and 109 acres of meadow land.)

As there were no roads in the fields, and the harvested fields were used for grazing, it was impossible to let one person get behind in harvesting. At planning time, too, the field would be ploughed, and seeds scattered and covered with soil by a harrow, but as there were no roads in the fields, if one person was late in planting, it would be impossible to seed his field. Therefore, the time of planting and harvesting had to be decided at the village meeting, and there was no way the decision could be disobeyed. Of all the jobs in the field the most important were ploughing and harvesting. Ploughing took place before the planting of barley in April and wheat in September, and, in addition, in the fallow fields in June and

FIG. 18. SQUARE FIELD NEAR PADUA IN THE
NORTHERN ITALY.

Source : Combirdge Economic History, 1941, 110.

July. These times were decided at the village meeting.
The use of the permanent pasture land, the meadow land,
forest, and rivers and other community matters were dis-
cussed and decided at the village meeting. This kind of

40

FIG. 19. MEARSTONES AND BOUNDARY STAKES OF FIELDS

Source : C. S. & C. S. Orwin 1954, *Plate* 24.

social organization is referred to as a "rural community."

The earliest written evidence of the three-field system appears in Schwaben (now southwest Germany) in 789, eleven years before Charlemagne was crowned emperor by Pope Leo III.

The three-field system spread and by the thirteenth century had reached most areas in northwest Europe. (On the other hand, Mediterranean areas continued to use the two-field system, and some do even today.) The diffusion of the three-field system meant the diffusion of the social system of the rural community.

But the evolution from the clan system to the rural community did not occur naturally; it was politically motivated. The persons or families who distinguished themselves in the process of the dissolution of the clan system strongly promoted this change. In remaking the clan system as the slave system, they made themselves feudal lords. Using the rural communities they had established, these feudal lords successfully organized the serf system.

41

FIG. 20. FRENCH CASTLE

Source : Heibonsha 1966, Vol. 11, 756.

The establishment of this rural community was also the establishment of the three-field system, and the three-field system was really equivalent to a medieval agricultural revolution, because of its rapid beneficial effect on production levels. And the clan chiefs under the clan system organized the serf-system in order to benefit from the increasing production resulting from the so-called medieval agricultural revolution.

But life was not always peaceful for the new feudal lord. He ruled over people who used to be his equals as family heads and were now treated as serfs, and there was no knowing when he himself might be overthrown. And so what was the answer ?

It seems that men basically think alike at almost any point in history. In Japanese political parties there are both conservative and reformist elements who form cliques. This is a way of "borrowing the shadow of a big tree" and strengthening one's own position. And the family chief, elevated to feudal lord, decided to find a "large shadow" to protect him from his neighboring feudal lords.

So the feudal lord presented his land to a more powerful lord and became his vassal. Then the lord nominally returned the land to the vassal. This land was called a feudal fief. But a vassal had all kinds of duties toward his lord, perhaps the most important of which was in a time of emergency raising an army at his own expense. Under these conditions the vassal could keep his land indefinitely. Each feudal fief was not only an independent, self-supporting agricultural unit but also a politically independent unit (country). The lord received various crops from serfs, allotted them work and at the same time acted as chief of police and court judge. This economic and political unit was called a manor. The lord was head of the manor.

To protect his position, the manor lord became a vassal to an even more powerful lord. In this way, through the feudal fief relationship, the chain stretched finally to the royal household. And the king, in turn, had been appointed by the pope. The appointing of kings with oil by a prophet or God's representative was a Jewish custom from Old Testament times. In this case, the pope played the role of a Hebrew prophet. In this way internal government formed a pyramid with the king at the apex. This was the European feudal system.

But this was not like the centralized and firmly controlled government of Rome. There were many manors, and whether a manor was large or small, each lord was a "king" in his own territory. So the European feudal system was not under the centralized and powerful control, but under local political rule. The unifying ruler was, of course, the king, who differed from ordinary lords only in his authority to make foreign policy, administer the death penalty, and settle major internal problems.

FIVE

The Growth of Feudal Society in Japan

In Chapter 4 we studied the growth of feudal society in Europe and found that the feudal society had elements of both the central government system (fief system) developed in the dry zone, and the local government system (serf system) developed in the humid zone. The former remained an ideology and the latter became reality. If the former had actually come about, it would have been impossible to establish a feudal society. In this chapter I want to study the growth of feudal society in Japan. In East Asia also, the imperial rule of the Han and Tang dynasties spread from China to almost the entire area, just as the Roman Empire spread in the Middle East and Europe. Only Japan escaped coming under the actual rule of the Han and Tang dynasties. Nevertheless, she influenced by their ideology. Japan, as a humid agricultural area, developed a feudal system, but other humid areas like South China and Korea were ruled by Chinese imperialism (which developed in the northern dry area) and so they didn't develop feudalism. Japan first learnt from the Chinese imperial system of statutes and began compiling its own in the seventh century. She completed the task in 701. The statutes underwent revision and amendment, but essentially remained until the Meiji Restoration (1868) roughly a millennium later.

These statutes were an imitation of the Chinese, especially Tang dynasty, legal system. But there was one

FIG. 21. HIMEJIZYO : THE MOST BEAUTIFUL CASTLE IN
JAPAN

Source : Heibonsha 1966, Vol. 11. 755.

fundamental difference between the two systems. In
Japan, the most powerful person in the legal system, the
emperor, also had a religious position as a *kami* (god).
On the other hand, Chinese Emperors were regarded as
human beings. But despite the establishment of a legal
system, the clan system was still dominate, that is, without the politically and religiously powerful emperor, the
statute system would not have had the strength to survive. Nevertheless, the statute system served as the base
for the subsequent Japanese Government.

But after about the tenth century the system began to
decline and was replaced by Japan's unique *samurai*, that
is, feudal law, system. The statutes more or less became
absolete and were only retained as a thread of imperial
life in Kyōto. In other words, the statute system lost all
actual power and only exsisted as theoretical authority.
Without the establishment of the statute system the feudal system would never have appeared. The reason is that

without central type of government of the statute system, the developed manor political system could not have made an adequate form of government.

It is said that at the end of the twelfth century Japan changed from a statute government to a feudal government. But both before and after the change, feudal lords of manors, formed a bureaucracy based on the system of national laws. The actual change was slight. In act they continued to wield power, but outside the law. And the retired *dajō-daijin,* who were at the highest level and should have protected the statute system, ignored it and held manors themselves. But if they had completely ignored the statute system, it would have been difficult to defend their manors against their fellows. Without preserving a facade of keeping the statute system, Japan would have fallen into anarchy.

The Warring States Period is only explicable if we assume the continuation of the statute system. True, the system lost nearly all its authority before the period — which is why the unified government had been destroyed — but during the period *samurai* speculated about the chances of reuniting the country by allying themselves with the emperor or the statute system. Their attempts to join forces with the emperor show that the statute system was not useless.

In the Tokugawa, or Edo Period (1603 - 1867), the powerful leader of the Tokugawa family, who had robbed power from the Toyotomi family, was given the title "shogun" by the emperor. Also, the emperor nominally appointed *daimyos,* to positions outlined in the statutues, for example, *Echizen-no-kami* (governor of Echizen Province) and *Satsuma-no-kami* (governor of Satsuma Province).

The facade of the statute system was rule of the people by the emperor through a bureaucracy. But inevitably the statute system was forced to compromise on various points with the clan system. For example, the framers of the statute system did not adopt the Chinese system of national examinations for recruitment to the bureaucracy. Instead, they made it a monopoly of the already ruling classes. This, of course, prevented the completion of a true bureacratic organization. And through this "gap" in the "imitation" statute system arose the manor system. The manors neither paid taxes to the government nor admitted government officials. In fact they were completely separate from the statute system.

Under the statute system, all land officially belonged to the state. Every six years the government distributed the land according to a fresh census. Land so distributed was called *kubunden*. If a peasant died, his land reverted to the state. Recipients of *kubunden* incurred certain obligations : payment of land tax, in rice and other products, and participation in public-works projects. As I explained earlier, the land and the peasants were owned by the state, and even when a peasant cleared new land, it was the property of the state. But in fact, under the leadership of the head of the large family (*gōko*), small families (*bōko*) cultivated land. Therefore, the social system was very similar to clanship. The clan chiefs still controlled the position of governor in the ancient bureacracy, even if all land belonged to the government, and their private ownership of land was recognized. Meanwhile, the temples and shrines prospered because of gifts of land from the state and aristocrats, and kept many slaves just like the latter. To effectively manage the *kubunden* system it was necessary to increase the amount of land in proportion to the increase in the number of farmers. So the government made efforts to reclaim the wasteland and to encourage reclamation by private individuals. The government freed private persons who reclaimed land, their sons, and their grandsons from taxation, and in 743 the government made the tax waiver permanent. As a result, the reclamation of land became very popular, and top government officials worked hard to support land reclamation. In effect, the government was contributing to the breakup of its monopoly of land. Burdened with heavy taxes, many peasants fled to aristocrats', large temples', and shrines' estates, where they were illegally employed.

The amount of private land increased all over Japan. People not only reclaimed private land, but also occupied national land, *kubunden*. Their land was called *myōden*, and their owners were named *myōshu*, meaning "owner of a myōden." *Myōden* varied in size from one to ten hectares, but parcels of land of this size were easily controlled by the imperial government, and the *myōshu* presented his *myōden* to feudal lords, who were given the privilege of a tax exemption by the imperial government. These tax-exempt lands were called *shōen*, which means manor. The privilege of manors was recognized by the imperial government, and subsequently manors developed rapidly.

There were two kinds of manors at the time : one was developed by feudal lords themselves, and the other was contributed by people to feudal lords. In the eighth century the former outnumbered the latter, but after the ninth century, the latter increased. The reader may wonder why large manors managed by feudal lords themselves did not develop in Japan along the lines of the latifundia in Rome, though the number of contributed manors increased rapidly in number. I think the reason mainly lies in the character of Japanese agriculture or in the character of the Japanese climate. As I explained earlier, if labor is intensive, hoeing-type agriculture is more productive than fallow-type agriculture. So agriculture was developed by the intensity of labor rather than by the enlargement of farms. Also, the slavery system indispensable to the latifundium could not be developed in Japan.

How was a *myōden* managed ? As agriculture developed, the *myōden* became established in the tenth century, and from the eleventh to the thirteenth century it

48

FIG. 22. JAPANESE MANOR

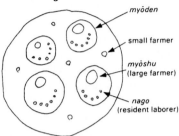

myōden

small farmer

myōshu
(large farmer)

nago
(resident laborer)

evolved into the basic element of the manor (Fig. 22). The new large family included the *dōzoku* (members of the same blood) and slaves. Feudal lords who lived in Kyōto and Nara dispatched men from those cities to manage their manors or appointed local leaders to manage them. Almost all the local leaders who presented their developed lands to feudal lords and were in turn appointed managers were more independent than managers sent from the feudal lords.

In addition, these local leaders kept their own armies to defend their *myōden* against attacks by neighbors or against usurption by neighbors or the government.

The local leaders were under the leadership of the family head and formed a strong familylike unit. The fundamental elements of this faction system came from the ancient system and remained especially strong in eastern Japan, where lands were energetically reclaimed. From the tenth century, these local leaders did not present their lands to feudal lords who lived in Kyōto or Nara, but to the descendants of loyal families — the Minamoto, Taira, etc. — who were sent as chiefs of the local governments from the central imperial government in Kyōto, and after finishing their appointments continued to live in the location of the local government. The local leaders presented their lands to them and received their family names (Minamoto, Taira, etc.) and as a result were counted as members of their families. These various factions grew and came to feud with each other.

First, Taira no Kiyomori, chief of the Taira faction, usurped the political power of the court nobility in the capital of Kyōto. Afterwards, Minamoto no Yoritomo, chief of the Minamoto faction, gained control and established a military-class government (shogunate) far from Kyōto, in Kamakura in eastern Japan, in 1183. This was the establishment of a feudal society in Japan.

So there were two governments in Japan : the imperial government of the court nobility in Kyōto and the shogunate in Kamakura.

The imperial government gave the Kamakura Shogunate the right to appoint samurai, *shugo,* and *jitō* throughout Japan. A *shugo* was appointed to each province, and he controlled all samurai in his province and kept public order. A *jitō* collected land taxes from the farmers on the manors and sent them to the absent feudal lords of these manors, and was given a part of their land taxes as his salary. Therefore, the lands were controlled by both government.

The relationship between the shogun, the head of the shogunate, and his vassals was very similar to the family system. Also, it clearly shows characteristics of the hoeing-type agricultural society. All vassals were local leaders who had their own developed lands, and the Kamakura Shogunate defended their landownership, as well as gave them new lands and appointed them to the position of jitō of the manors of feudal lords living in Kyōto or Nara. Amongst these vassals there were various kinds of landowners. The vassals with the largest plots of land resembled feudal lords while the vassals with the smallest plots of land had the character of myōshu.

Below the *myōshu* were people who lived as slaves. They were called *nago* or *hikan.* Prohibited from working for themselves, they could only survive by working for the *myōshu*. The *myōshu* were paternalistic toward the nago. The *myōshu* depended on the *nago* and on escaped villagers for farm labor. Of course, in the village there were other families who had work apart from that done for the *myōshu*.

The *chōja*, wealthy man, who frequenctly appears in tales of the time, was in fact a *myōshu*. On the outskirts of Tottoi city there is a pretty lake called Koyamaike. Long ago a powerful *chōja* lived in that area. One day he tried to sow a large rice paddy by using *nago* labor. The sun began to set over the western hills and it was reflected in the water of the unplanted portion of the paddy. Using the fan he was carrying, he stopped the sun from sinking until the planting was over. When he arose the next morning, he discovered that he paddy field had become a large lake, present Koyamaike, according to the legend. *Chōja* with large farms seem to have been common at the time.

From the fourteenth to the sixteenth century, the *chōja* gradually released their grip over the management of their farms, and gave some managerial responsibility to the nago. But they did not transfer all managerial responsibility, so the nago did not receive enough land to enable them to become completely independent. The nago eked out a living from the land they managed plus their remuneration for working for the myōshu.

In the thirteenth and fourteenth centuries there were continual quarrels about land taxes between the samurai living at the manors and the feudal lords in Kyōto and Nara. The samurai encroached more and more upon the manors, and by the fiteenth and sixteenth centuries, they occupied all the territory, completly excluding the influence of the feudal lords in Kyōto and Nara. This shows the destruction of the manor system and, as a result, daimyo were established.

As time passed, the nago became independent farmers

and beneath them again were other tenant farmers. As the number of people between daimyos and farmers increased, the financial position of the former grew worse and worse. Toyotomi Hideyoshi removed the middlemen and made the manor a unit directly responsible to the government. He did that all over the country. As a result, the village system of the Edo Period (1603-1867) began.

SIX

Absolute Monarchy in Europe and Japan

In the previous two chapters, we have looked at the growth of feudal societies in Europe and Japan. Here I would like to deal with the last stage of feudal society. In Europe, the last stage of feudal society was called "absolute monarchy."

About the absolute monarchies in France and England, John Nef (1940) says : medieval monarchs had power but nevertheless were not autocratic rulers. Autocratic rule is not a medieval style of rule, but rather a modern one. In the sixteenth century the French and English monarchies worked towards the extension of their power by suppressing local powers or compelling their cooperation. The monarchies planned to transform medieval government into modern absolutism. At the end of the fifteenth century, according to the Spanish ambassador in London in a report to his government, the English king, Henry VII (founder of the absolute monarchy), "wanted to rule England as his counterpart ruled France, but could not manage it." From this we can see that at that time the French king was stronger than the English one. But the same Spanish ambassador reported of Henry VII that the king's rule is in all ways strong.

One clue to the success of the absolute monarchies of France and England was the extension of the scope of their recognized powers, that is, the acquired regional powers were recognized as an extension of the monarchy's power. Another clue was the faithful execution of the king's will by the palace bureaucracy. In order to implement various policies the kings of France and England depended on two social classes : in the provinces the wealthy landowners (the gentry) and in the towns the wealthy merchants. Both these classes formed the backbone of the king's bureaucratic method of ruling.

In the 100 years between 1540 and 1640 the gradual mixing of these classes was fairly fast in England, but much slower in France. The reason is that the French king deprived them of their local and individual advantages. This didn't happen in England. The French monarch first created a new lower level of aristocracy, the members of which paid money for their social position and made their entire lives dependent on the king. Next he transferred government officials from their native areas where they had made their money. In England, royal administrators were mostly unpaid, and the king relied on them to implement his will in the provinces. These people worked essentially as volunteers, and if they disliked the king's orders, they ignored them. As a result, during the period of absolute monarchy, England industrialized before France.

During the Reformation, the kings of England and France didn't have a clear relationship with industry. But the success of the future autocratic government depended on the king's control of the economic system, in particular, on his ability to collect revenue. At the same time, the king had to protect the common man's profits. If the "nation state" government attempted to replace the feudal-and-ecclesiastical-type local or independent town governments, then it would have to guarantee to protect the citizens in the same way. Subjects, especially in poorer areas, believed this was the king's duty. Another belief was that if the king expected the people to work towards creating industry, then he should be prepared to invest money.

There were two methods the king used for enlarging his power to govern industry. One was to control the various conditions of employment. The other was to maintain a close relationship with industry and lead its development.

The above-mentioned are Nef's main ideas on the French and English systems of absolute monarchy. In brief, the typical medieval feudal government ruled by delegating authority to the provinces; the king was not a centralized autocrat. In the sixteenth century the English and French kings (of course, they were also feudal lords) depended on two new classes for control — in the country, the wealthy landed gentry and in the towns, the rich merchants. From the fourteenth and fifteenth centuries, commerce began to develop in England and France, and rich merchants and rich landowners appeared in the towns and country. Landowners rented the land from feudal lords and leased the land to tenant farmers. At first the feudal lords tried to exclude the landowners, but after realizing that their exclusion was impossible, they supported the landowners to be sure of receiving rent from them. By enlarging their control of local government and industry, the lords attempted to establish centralized autocracy. In short, absolute monarchy was centralized feudalism. If one accepts this explanation of absolute monarchy, in Japan absolute monarchy did not begin with the Meiji Restoration (1868) but in the Tokugawa Period (1603-1867).

But until now, no Japanese historian has claimed that Tokugawa Shogunate was an absolute monarchy. Tokuzō Fukuda is the sole exception, though his concept of absolute monarchy is not clear. He wrote *The Social and Economic Development of Japan* (1900) while a student of Lujo Brentano in Germany. In fact, this astute comparative history of Europe and Japan can be considered a joint work of the two men. The book is neglected today but as an economic history of Japan using the method of comparative history I think it deserves to be reappraised.

Fukuda proposed that during the Tokugawa Period Japan was an autocratic police state, that the period was not feudal. "The common claim," he wrote, "seems to be that 1603-1868 ... was the pinnacle of Japanese feudalism. This was first proposed by a Japanese scholar, and European scholars soon agreed, and that idea became generally accepted. But I believe that this idea is a mistake. This kind of mistake derives from the idea that the Japanese feudal system was destroyed by the Meiji Restoration, as English feudalism was destroyed by Cromwell, French feudalism was destroyed in 1789, and German feudalism was destroyed in 1851. If it is claimed that the period 1603-1868 was the height of Japanese feudalism, then, by the same token, France from Louis XI and Richelieu to 1789 and Germany from Kurfuerst to 1848 are similarly peak periods in feudalism. In these periods the form of feudalism continued, but the new, modern central government had begun to take shape over its remains. Powerful lords lost their previous independence and became instruments of the new central government. This period between feudalism and the establishment of a strong central government was a necessary though indistinct interval."

Fukuda claimed that the Tokugawa Period was not a period of feudalism, because he thought of it as a system of devolved government. Judging from the examples he offered in comparison, France, England, and Germany, one can say that he regarded the Tokugawa Period as an absolute monarchy. According to him the absolute monarchy was the continuation of feudalism but with a true central government (that is a centralized feudal government). Fukuda described the Tokugawa style of government as follows; "In the Tokugawa Period, the shogun entrusted local political power to daimyos throughout Japan, but their power to make law only concerned minor matters. Important matters were decided directly by the shogun. In this way the daimyos were all ruled by the Tokugawa central government, and the shogun, appointed by the Emperor, was not only the most powerful lord, but at the same time the leader of the samurai class. If a daimyo made a mistake then the shogun soon intervened, and if he misbehaved politically he lost his power. This foundation of central government laid by Tokugawa Ieyasu, the first shogun, was further worked on by Tokugawa Iemitu, the third shogun, who established the following penalties for daimyos :

(1) the imposition of a heavy financial burden in the form of, say, a major construction project
(2) forced transfer of power to the daimyo's successor
(3) transfer to a fief with a smaller rice yield
(4) deprivation of daimyo rank or *seppuku*

Apart from these penalties, Iemitsu established *sankin-kōtai*, a system in which every daimyo was required to reside in Edo in alternate years. Thus a daimyo maintained in Edo a home, at which, moreover, his family permanently resided as *de facto* hostages to guarantee his loyalty. The system also kept the daimyo in financial difficulty by requiring him to maintain a second home in Edo etc.

The marriage of a daimyo or his adoption of children also had to be approved by the shogun. He also needed the shogun's permission to give his land to his son. Without the shogunate's permission he could not build a new castle or repair an old one. He had to pay various tributes to the shogunate and had to maintain a reasonable military force for emergencies. He could not make direct contact with foreign countries and he was forbidden to build large ships.

Especially strict laws governed the relationship between a daimyo and the emperor. Even if summoned by the emperor, a daimyo was forbidden to enter the palace. The daimyos of western Japan were not allowed to pass through Kyōto, the location of the palace, on the way to and from Edo. If a daimyo secretly visited the capital and his visit was discovered, he was stripped of daimyo rank, no matter how important a personage he was. If a daimyo wanted to visit Kyōto, he needed the prior permission of the Shogunate. The Tokugawa successfully destroyed feudal govenment and broke the feudal spirit through these legion rules and restrictions, though at the same time they tried to maintain the general appearance of feudalism.

That is Tokuzō Fukuda's description of the Tokugawa Period. He concludes that power and authority were separate : power was vested in the Shogunate, authority in the emperor.

Then how did the Tokugawa Shogunate achieve such a strong centralized power ?. The most important reason was its broad capital base. Of the annual nationwide crop of 30 million *koku* (1 koku=4.9 bushels) of rice, the government owned 7 million, or 23 percent. The daimyos in hereditary vassalage to the Tokugawa owned 9.4 million koku, and the other daimyos 9.3 million koku. Thus the Shogunate, which also received contributions of rice from areas under its direct administration, controlled over half of the total crop.

Also, the Shogunate exercised strict control over industry. But most important was the state of national isolation. This had two effects. On one hand it stopped the daimyos from amassing wealth from foreign trade (though the two clans Satsuma and Chōshū who finally defeated the Shogunate got their money from secret foreign trade), and on the other hand it made it possible for the Shogunate alone to profit from foreign trade. The absolute monarchies in France and England also held special privileges due to feudal lords, and these became their monopolies, which were reorganized and consolidated. There were the so-called special powers of the monarchy (king's privileges), and it was the job of the bureaucracy to administer them. G. R. Elton calls this type of government "fiscal feudalism." In addition, there was the right of first purchase. The lord had the right to buy a certain percentage of the production at a special low rate. During the Tokugawa Period, a period of national isolation, this first purchase right of the shogun can be seen as another special monarchical power.

After the rule of Tokugawa Ieyasu, the shogunate had a monopoly on coin minting and money printing, though one or tow leading clans were allowed to print money for use within their fiefs. Also, merchants were allowed to form and administer their own guilds. The shogunate also standardized weights and measures, coordinated transportation, and carefully maintained internal law and order. For example, during the shogunate of Iemitsu, an investigation was undertaken into the political state of daimyos, and citizens' complaints were heard. This is one reason why Fukuda called Tokugawa Japan an "autocratic police state."

Another reason the Tokugawa Shogunate was able to exercise such power over local daimyos was the *kokudaka,* or rice yield, system, under which an estimate was made of the productivity of a fief. Under Toyotomi Hideyoshi, the system was implemented throughout the country. The system, by fixing taxes, helped the Tokugawa Shogunate to control the entire country.

In *Japan's Emergence As a Modern State* Herbert Norman wrote : "This late feudalism represents one of the most conscious attempts in history to freeze society in a rigid hierarchical mold. Every social class, and every subdivision within it, had its own regulations covering all the minutiae of clothing, ceremony and behavior, which had to be strictly observed on pain of punishment."

The "rigid hierarchical mold" of Tokugawa society was fiercely defended. Rank in the hierarchy system was based on kokudaka, rice yield, because agriculture was the main industry of the time. Of course, apart from kokudaka there many secondary factors in determining rank

TABLE 3 **CHRONOLOGICAL TABLE OF JAPANESE POLITICS AND CULTURE**

Period	Date	Event
NON. EARTHEN. WARE AGE (PRE. JOMON)	20,000 B. C.	Hunting and fishing with stone implements made by striking
	8,000	
JOMON PERIOD	B. C.	Hunting and fishing with stone implements made by grinding
		Straw-rope patterned earthenware used
	400 B. C.	Rice cultivation begins
YAYOI PERIOD	57 A. D.	King of the country of Na in Japan offers tribute to Later Han
	188(?)	Himiko becomes queen of country of Yamatai
KOFUN PERIOD	300 391	The Yamato Court unifies Japan
		Japanese army fights three Korean countries
ASUKA PERIOD	538	Buddhism introduced
	604	Constitution of 17 Articles
	607	Horyuji Temple constructed
	630	First envoys dispatched to T'ang
	645	Taika Reforms
NARA PERIOD	710	Nara established as capital
	712	*Kojiki* (Record of Ancient Matters) compiled
	720	*Nihonshoki* (Chronicles of Japan) compiled
	741	Imperial edict for construction of *kokubun-ji* and *kokubun-niji*
		(state-established provincial temples and convents)
		Manyoshu compiled
HEIAN PERIOD	794	Kyoto-established as capital
	805	Saicho introduces Tendai sect
	806	Kukai introduces Shingon sect
	828	Kukai establishes Shugei-shuchi In (first public educational institution)
	857	Fujiwara power over Court increases
	905	*Kokin Waka-shu*, poetry anthology
	1000	*Makura no Soshi* ("The Pillow Book") written
	1011	*Genji Monogatari* ("Tales of Genji") completed
	1086	In (government by an ex-emperor) begins
		Samurai power increases
	1167	Taira no Kiyomori becomes Dajo-daijin (Prime Minister)
	1180 to	Battles between the Minamoto and Taira
	1185	Taira destroyed
	1190	Eisai propagates Rinzai sect of Zen
KAMAKURA PERIOD	1192	Minamoto no Yoritomo establishes Kamakura Shogunate
	1219	Minamoto no Sanetomo assassinated
	1224	Jodo-shin-shu sect spreads
	1227	Dogen introduces Soto sect of Zen
	1253	Nichiren preaches the Lotus Sutra
	1274	First Mongol invasion
	1281	Second Mongol invasion
	1331	Court splits into Northern and Southern Courts (*Nanboku Cho* begins)
	1331 to	War between Emperor Go-Daigo and Kamakura Shogunate
	1333	Kamakura Shogunate destroyed

60

MUROMACHI PERIOD	1338	Ashikaga Takauji established Muromachi Shogunate
	1392	Unification of Northern and Southern Courts
	1406(?)	Zeami completes *Kaden-sho* ("Quintessance of Noh")
	1467	Onin War : The Age of Civil Wars begins
	to 1477	Frequency of agrarian uprisings increase
	1543	Introduction of firearms from Portugal
	1549	Introduction of Christianity
	1573	Oda Nobunaga banishes Ashikaga shogun Ashikaga Shogunate destroyed
AZUCHI MOMOYAMA PERIOD	1573	Nobunaga assumes hegemony
	1582	Nobunaga assassinated Christian feudal lords send young envoys to Rome
	1585	Toyotomi Hideyoshi unifies country Tea ceremony becomes popular
	1587	Christianity prohibited
	1600	Battle of Sekigahara
EDO PERIOD	1603	Tokugawa Ieyasu establishes Tokugawa Shogunate in Edo Kabuki plays performed
	1614	Battle of Winter
	1615	Battle of Summer
	1637	Shimabara Rebellion
	1639	National isolation policy enacted
	1682	*Koshoku Ichidai Otoko* ("The Man who Spent his Life at Love Affairs")
	1693	*Narrow Road to the Deep North* written by Basho
	1702	47 loyal *ronin* avenge their lord's death
	1703	*Ningyo-joruri* (bunraku) by Chikamatsu Monzaemon performed
	1853	Commodore Perry lands in Japan
	1854	Japan concludes amity treaties with America, Britain and Russia
	1855	Japan concludes amity treaties with France and Holland
	1867	Tokugawa Shogunate destroyed
MEIJI PERIOD	1868	Meiji Restoration

in the hierarchy system. For example, amongst samurai there were immediate followers of the shogun and indirect vassals, and amongst daimyos there were hereditary vassals and non-hereditary vassals. But it hardly needs to be said that kokudaka was the ultimate factor in ranking.

Kokudaka originally meant the harvest of rice paddies but in due course it came to include the yield of field crops, timber, wild nuts, berries, etc., and river and sea products. The taxable sum was paid in actual tributes or in labor according to fixed rates based on kokudaka. How did the kokudaka system begin? The earliest reference to the system is in 1488, in the archives of the

Kyōgoku family of Ōmi (Shiga Prefecture). Nobunaga and Hideyoshi, his vassal, both owned lands in Ōmi and used the system there. After Hideyoshi surveyed his land, the system spread all over Japan.

In this way, through the kokudaka the Shogunate governed both daimyos and peasants and formed them into a solid unit. In both England and France the absolute monarchies were destroyed after 150 years from the inside by the landed gentry and merchants (that is, the bourgeois revolution). But in Japan the situation continued for over 250 years. That is, the gentry and merchants did not become powerful enough to destroy the absolute monarchy from the inside. But this does not deny that the Tokugawa were absolute monarchists. On the contrary, it shows how well developed was the Japanese absolute monarchy.

Here I have been mainly concerned with proving that the Tokugawa Period was a period of absolute monarchy, but I would also like to make clear comparisons between the English, French, and Japanese systems of absolute monarchy. As I have said, the absolute monarchy was a centralized monarchial feudal system, and bureaucracy became an essential part of the system. The Tokugawa bureaucracy was especially well organized.

The political executives, rōjū, or their superios, the tairō, directed other officials to control the affairs of state and to command the daimyos. Below the rōjū the wakadoshiyori controlled the hatamoto and gokenin (direct retainers of the shogun). The sōshaban were responsible for organizing the ceremony when a daimyo went to Edo castle. The kōke were in charge of imperial ceremonies. The sobashū and sobayōnin kept the shogun informed of political affairs. The rusui took care of Edo castle when the shogun was away and of the palace where his family lived. The ōbangashira led the group of ōban (hatamoto). The ōmetsuke directed the daimyos, and metsuke directed the retainers of the shogun . The jishabugyō took charge

62

of temples and shrines, and the *machibugyō* managed town politics in Edo. Within the *kanjōbugyō*, the *kanjōgata* controlled the politics of the Kantō area and the directly owned Tokugawa lands, and the *kujigata* ran legal affairs. Apart from these, there were *gungai* and *daikan* as local political agents.

Compared with this type of bureaucracy, the English and French absolute monarchies were behind. On the other hand, a parliamentary system evolved in England and France but not in Tokugawa Japan. In Japan a bureaucratic system existed in the feudal period before the Tokugawa Period, and, in France and England there was a parliamentary system in the feudal period before the absolute monarchies. If one views the bureaucracy as a vertical style of government, then the parliamentary system is a horizontal "contract" system. The difference between the Japanese and European political systems is linked with the difference between the agricultural systems, that is, the difference between a fallow-type agricultural society and a hoeing-type agricultural society.

63

SEVEN

Squire Monarchy and the Industrial Revolution in England and Japan

For more than fifty years many Japanese historians have disputed the nature of the Meiji Restoration. Some have insisted that it was a bourgeois revolution that destroyed feudal society, while others have insisted that it was the beginning of absolute monarchy, which can be the last stage of feudalism. After the Meiji Restoration, there certainly remained many feudal elements in Japanese society. Although some scholars insist that these elements were uninfluential, others insist that they continued to affect society.

G. R. Elton offers an interesting opinion in his *Tudor Revolution in Government*. He postulates that there were three administrative revolutions in England : the first revolution was the establishment of royal feudal states in the eleventh century ; the second was the establishment of a monarchic nation-state in the sixteenth century ; the third was the establishment of a parliamentary democracy in the nineteenth century. The Civil War (the bourgeois revolution, 1640-60), which occurred between the establishment of a monarchic nation-state and the establishment of parliamentary democracy did not change the administrative principles but only resulted in the application of the paternal Tudor state to a parlimentary monarchy.

If Elton's first administrative stage (elevente-fifteenth centuries) was a feudal period and his third administrative stage (nineteenth century) was a capitalistic period, then his second administrative atage (sixteenth-eighteenth centuries) should be seen as a period of transition from feudalism to capitalism.

In the controversy about the Meiji Restoration, Japanese scholars are mistaken in thinking that the bourgeois revolution was the end of the transitional period. The Meiji Restoration marked the beginning of, the second half of the transitional period. It is obvious, therefore, that many feudal elements would remain to influence society.

Of course the bourgeois revolution destroyed feudal society, abolished feudal privileges, and established the rights of private property. But nevertheless, before it there had been many capitalistic elements that greatly influenced feudal society and after it many feudal remnants that influenced capitalistic society. Usually, the first half of the transitional period is called an absolute monarchy, and I would like to call the second half of the period a "squire monarchy," because this was the stage in which landowners acquired political power and controlled the government.

As described above, in an absolute monarchy the king monopolized all privileges in his status as a feudal lord and used those privileges to wrest political and economic power from rich merchants in the town and rich landowners in the country. In order to utilize his privileges he introduced a bureaucracy and changed from being a feudal lord to being the leader of a centralized national bureaucracy. The bureaucracy still depended financially on the manors, but as an English national representative he received an income, partly from foreign trade, to cover marriages with foreign royal families, foreign wars, and other large incidental expenses, and by an agreement with parliament he could be granted a special tax raised from the richest classes of the nation. Therefore, under an absolute monarchy, the bureaucracy was both a centralized national institution and also the king's own household management.

Even after the Civil War, the nature of the bureaucracy remained unchanged for a long time. During the Civil War, the king's manors were confiscated by Parliament and not returned after the Restoration (1660). Instead Parliament imposed taxes on the people and gave the king almost the same income that he had received from his manors. The source of national finance changed as a result from the income of the king's manors to the income from taxes levied on the people in the Civil War. That is, feudal finance changed into modern finance. But there was still no differentiation between the king's household budget and the national budget, and so all ministers, ambassadors, generals, admirals, etc. were seen as the king's servants. The prime minister of the cabinet was the king himself, and the other ministers could only act as advisers to the king. Until the reformation of Parliament at the beginning of the nineteenth century, national finance was not separated into the king's household budget and the national budget, and the king's servants were not public servants.

Under an absolute monarchy, commerce and industry developd based on the monopolies given by the king. At that time the most important industry was the woolen industry and its accompanying trade. English farmers bred sheep and sent the fleeces to the woolen industries in the towns. But in the sixteenth and seventeenth centuries many farmers began to handle the wool themselves rather than send it to the merchants in town. In this way, wool merchants without monopoly rights began to trade wool produced domestically by farmers again without monopoly rights. Many attempts were made by the government to stop this illicit trade, but they failed. Rich landowners, who were appointed royal justices of peace in rural areas, were themselves involved in this industry and trade, and therefore did little to prohibit it.

Competition between commerce and industry with monopolies (based on the king's privileges) and those without monopolies became steadily fiercer. In addition, friction between feudal lords with privileges and landowners without them exacerbated the situation. Finally, the tensions were relieved in the Civil War, and the king's privileges were at last abolished.

After the Civil War, political power was usurped by these rich landowners and merchants, and it is this which I call squire monarchy. National finances relied on income from taxes, especially the land tax imposed on landowners because the most important industry at time was agriculture. In return, the rich landowners who paid the heavy land tax monopolized the right to elect or become members of the House of Commons (for example, between 1711 and 1831, these rights were monopolized by the landowners whose annual land rents were above £600 in the country and £300 in the towns). In 1689 the corn law was introduced giving the landowner a bounty of 5 shillings when the price of one quarter of wheat was below 48 shillings (for example, in 1697-1765, the government gave the landowners a total £6,058,962 in corn bounties.)

The woolen industry was managed as part of the manufacturing system. The industry was divided into three processes : spinning and weaving, performed in the farmers' domestic industries, and finishing, done at the manufacturers' workshops by tool rather than machine. Since the demand for wool fluctuated sharply and the supply of the materials (wool and wool yarn) was very unstable, the constant long-term employment of laborers was undesirable for the manufacturer. The domestic industry of the farmer was much more attractive for the manufacturer, because the farmer could be dismissed any time. The greatest part of the capital of the woolen industry was the workers' wages. In a mechanized factory, the price of each product decreases as the size of the factory increases, but in the contemporary manufacturing system the price increased and competitive power decreased as the system grew larger. The manufacturing system was unable to enlarge the size of the business. Also, at that time the trade in woolen textiles was very unstable and dangerous and required long-term capital investment. Small textile manufactures were always controlled by larger merchants which in turn shifted responsibility to the govenment. The government responded by forbidding the American and Irish texile industries and requiring the use of English ships to take textiles from England to America and Ireland. By the Civil War, the domestic monopolies of commerce and industry had been abolished, but afterwards the government indulged in international monopolies instead. One of the aims of the government in pressuring this policy towards the textile industry was the development of trade. As a result of increased demand, the manufacturing industry was mechanized from about 1760 (that is, the industial revolution). Also the domestic industry system amongst farmers had become too large and too difficult to manage. When a machine factory was built in the town, the migration of workers from the country to the town was necessary. As the number of industrial workers increased with the rapid development of the machine factory system, so, too, did the demand for agricultural products increase. To solve this problem the govenment introduced the enclosure policy.

The enclosure policy involved the gathering of several area into one farm, with hedges around the fields and roads leading to the main village street. This act was enforced at the beginning of the eighteenth century. If two thirds of the landowners in the village agreed to the enclosure system, it could be forced upon the dissenting members using this act. As the table 4 shows, enclosures were carried out rapidly between 1760 and the mid-nineteenth century. As a result there were scarcely any

Table 4 ENCLOSURE ACTS AND ENCLOSED AREAS IN
ENGLAND AFTER 1700

Year	Open Field & Field		Fields	
	Acts	Areas	Acts	Areas
1700-1760	152	237,845 acres	56	74,518 acres
1761-1801	1479	2,428,721	521	752,150
1802-1844	1075	1,610,302	808	939,043
after 1845	164	187,321	508	334,908
Total	2870	4,461,180	1893	2,100,617

Source : H. Johnson, 1909, 90.

rural communities left in mid-nineteenth century England. In the enclosed field system, people were undisturbed by their neighbors and were free to cultivate using the new four-year rotation (wheat → turnip → barley → clover). This was called Norfolk husbandry because it was begun in Norfolk in the end of the seventeenth and early eighteenth centuries.

As this method of farming produced a lot of turnips and clover as fodder, the farmers were able to stable livestock all year long (under the three-field system farmers could only stable livestock in winter). The quantity of manure produced also increased rapidly, and so pastures and meadows could be changed into fields. The yield of crops then increased by four or five times as much as under the three-field system (that is, the agricultural revolution). Large farmers were able to practice Norfolk husbandry on their enclosed lands, but small farmers did not have the money to hedge their strips of allocated land. They were also not able to produce enough, and so lost their common rights within the community. As a result they were forced to sell their land to a big farmer and become an agricultural or industrial laborer.

In the process of the industrial revolution, the political and social position of commercial capitalists was usurped

69

by the industrial capitalists, because the price of machine-made products decreased as the size of the factory increased. The position of landowners also worsened rapidly (for example, in England, the export of wheat was 1,667,140 quarters in 1750, just before the industrial revolution, but the import of wheat was 3,938,829 quarters in 1800, in the middle of the industrial revolution). But the landowners still did not lose thier political power and made moves to strengthen the corn laws rather than abolish them.

The capitalists who grew rapidly in the industrial revolution began to compete with the landowners and finally defeated them. The reformation of Parliament in 1832 and the abolition of the corn laws in 1846 were milestones in the struggle. With the abolition of the corn laws in 1846, the squire monarchy in England was finished, and a true capitalistic society under the control of industrial capitalists began. English squire monaochy can be said to have lasted for 186 years, from the Civil War (1640-1660) to the abolition of the corn laws (1846).

If the Tokugawa Period was the absolute monarchy and the Meiji Restration was the bourgeois revolution as I described in Chapter 6, the squire monarchy in Japan was between the Meiji Restration and the land reform directly following defeat in the Second World War. In the second half of the nineteenth century, the Japanese government established a policy of subsidizing industry through a land tax, because agriculture was the chief industry at that time. As a result, Japan's industrial revolution occurred at the end of the nineteenth century and the beginning of the twentieth century.

Japan's squire monarchy was controlled by the capitalist class and the landowner class. Almost all tenant farms were very small, but the rents paid in rice were very high (about 50 percent of the yield) ; therefore the tenant farmers were very poor, and they or their daughters were compelled to work in the factories, where their wages were very low. In short, the landowner class were able to charge high rents and convert rent money to industrial capital owing to the capitalist class. The capitalist class could get the capital and the cheap labor owing to the landowner class. As poor tenant farmers and laborers could scarcely purchase industrial goods, the capitalist class exported their industrial goods to foreign countries, especially Korea and China, where they met opposition from local capitalists. That led to the Pacific War. Within Japan high rents and low wages created trouble betwen tenant farmers and laborers, and the landowner and capitalist classes. The post war land refom deprived the landowner class of political influence, and the squire monarchy disappeared in Japan.

EIGHT

World Capitalism

As I pointed out in Chapter 7, English farmers had two sources of income : the domestic woolen industry and agriculture. As mechanized factories developed in the towns, farmers' lives were destroyed by the change from rural domestic industry to urban factories. Subsistence rural agriculture also changed into commercial agriculture catering to people in the towns (the English agricultural revolution).

The English Government wanted to disseminate the changes brought by the industrial revolution to other countries and employed the theory of international specialization. This theory divided countries into two kinds — those suitable for agricuiture and those suitable for industry. Under this scheme the former export agricultural products to the latter, and the latter export industrial goods to the former. (But there is a catch. Not all agricultural products are suitble for all countries, but any country has access to capital and labor, and is therefore suitable for industrial production. England was not the only country in the world suited to industry.)

By implementing this theory the English Government managed to destroy foreign industries and to change foreign agriculture. For example, in Germany, until English textiles were imported, farmers had two sources of income as in England : the domestic textile industry and agriculture. From the end of the eighteenth century, English

72

TABLE 5   **ENGLISH TARIFFS ON INDIAN COTTON CLOTHS, 1812-1832**

(% ad valorem)

	1812	1824	1832
Muslin	271/2	371/2	10
Calico	712/3	671/2	10
Other	271/3	50	20

Source : T. Nishimura, 19, 132.

textile imports ruined the German domestic textie industry and the rural community, and transformed subsistence agriculture into commercial wheat production for export to England. (That was the German agricultural revolution.)

I like to refer to this close relationship between England and Germany as "world capitalism." Towards the end of the eighteenth century and the beginning of the nineteenth century, world capitism spread to many parts of the world, with England as its center. The German textile industry was not, however, completely destroyed by the English textile industry. The industry survived in the more remote provinces of Germany, and those provinces were the base from which the German industrial revolution spread in the latter half of the nineteenth century.

I would like to look next at India, which was a British colony. In India, before it was absorbed into the system of world capitalism, the farmers had two sources of income, as in England and Germany. Cotton goods became the most important English export, but cotton was the traditional textile indutry in India. In the first half of the nineteenth century, the English Government used several methods to destroy it. For example, in spite of the English Government's insistence on free trade between all countries, it imposed a heavy customs duty on

73

TABLE 6 **EXPORT AND IMPORT OF CLOTH FROM INDIA, 1814-1834**

Year	Export to England pieces	Export to India yards
1814	1,266,603	818,203
1821	534,495	19,138,726
1828	422,504	42,822,077
1834	306,086	51,777,277

Source : T. Yanaihara, 1963, 562.

Indian cotton cloth and a heavy tax on the Indian cotton industry (Table 5). As a result, the price of Indian cotton goods rose by 15 to 17.5 percent.

In 1814, for example, India exported 1,266,608 pieces of cotton to England, but by 1834, India imported 51,777,277 yards of cotton cloth from England (Table 6). Since the Indian cotton industry had been destroyed, the people who has worked in it were forced to become tenant farmers, and that phenomenon caused a rapid rise in land rents. They could only pay such high rents to landowners by growing raw cotton for export to the English textile industry. The development of such a landowner system in India was encouraged by the establishment of Indian railways and credit institutions, by English merchants in Calcuta and Bombay, and by Indian merchants and usurers.

I would like to point out that the English machine factory system had a strong influence on German and Indian agriculture. In Germany, it established a capitalistic farm system with capitalist farmers using agricultural labores. But in India, it established a landowner system with landowners taking very high rent from tenant farmers. The reason for the difference was, I think, the difference between fallow-type agriculture using extensive

74

labor and hoeing-type agriculture using intensive labor.
The French and American agricultural and industrial
revolutions belonged to the German type, and capitalism
developed in all three countries, but in Japan these revolutions were a mixture of the German and Indian
types ; in Japan both capitalism and the landowner system developed. Just before Japan was forced to end its
200 years of isolation in 1858 by America, Japanese farmers, like farmers in England, Germany, and India, supported themselves in two ways. Japanese farm industries
(especially the cotton industry) were violently destroyed
by imported goods, but there was a difference between
advanced and less advanced areas. At that time cotton
was grown in most parts of Japan. In the more advanced areas spinning and weaving were managed by
different merchants, but in the less advanced areas one
merchant managed both processes. Therefore, when inexpensive machine-made cotton goods of excellent quality
were imported, the spinning industry in Japanese villages
died, and in less advanced areas the cotton industry itself
died out. In the more advanced areas, the weaving industry managed to survive by using imported yarn. After
the Meiji Restoration, spinning factories based on English
ones were established by the Japanese Government and
entrepreneurs, and these supplied cotton yarn to Japanese
weavers. In 1891 Japanese production of machine-made
cotton yarn exceeded imports, and in 1897 exports exceeded imports (Table 7). After that Japanese capitalism
developed rapidly mainly by the promotion of the cotton
industry.

On the other hand, in less advanced areas the cotton
industry was destroyed after 1858 and almost all farmers
lived only by growing foodstuffs. Because of this, an
Indian-type landowner system evolved, and farmers had
to pay high rents to owners in rice not money.

Subsistence agriculture evolved to a system to supply
towns and foreign countries. The main exports were

Table 7 PRODUCTION EXPORT, IMPORT AND CONSUMPTION OF COTTON YARN IN JAPAN, 1890-1900

(Kori ; 1 Kori=400 lb)

Year	Production	Import	Export	Consumption
1890	104,839	106,361	108	211,169
1891	144,980	57,792	109	202,664
1892	204,950	81,028	1,053	285,869
1893	214,758	64,684	11,796	278,389
1894	294,400	53,143	11,776	333,747
1895	366,689	48,637	11,776	403,550
1896	401,614	66,713	43,249	425,078
1897	511,236	53,636	140,116	424,756
1898	644,504	53,099	229,445	468,158
1899	757,315	27,369	341,202	443,482
1900	645,432	30,170	208,732	466,870

Source : Asahi Shimbunsha, 1966, 1213.

Table 8 JAPANESE AND KOREAN LARGE LANDOWNERS, 1919-1936

Year	100-200 hectares		more than 200 hectares	
	Korean	Japanese	Korean	Japanese
1919	360	321	180	169
1925	290	341	45	192
1931	319	361	49	187
1936	336	380	49	181

Source : Y. Taniura, 1966, 35.

silk, tea and rice. Until about 1880, in monetary terms, tea exports sometimes exceeded silk exports, but generally they were 70-80 percent of the latter. In the twentieth century tea exports declined rapidly because of Chinese and Indian tea. After about 1883 rice exports grew and in 1888 they exceeded tea exports. After 1858 tea exports continued to occupy second place, but from 1888 to 1898 rice was the leading export. Afterwards rice was imported to satisfy domestic demand, which had increased because of the Japanese industrial revolution. In the twentieth century, silk and cotton goods continued to occupy top positions amongst exports. To meet the sudden demand for rice, the Japanese Government began to import from Korea. The Korean agricultural revolution belonged to the Indian type. Until the end of the nineteenth century, Korean farmers, like British and Indian farmers, had two means of support. But after the victory in the Sino-Japanese War (1895), Japan exported machine-made cotton goods to Korea, completely destroying the domestic cotton industry. The Japanese Government pushed forward with its plans to colonize Korea, and succeeded in 1910. Between 1910 and 1918, Japan carried out a land survey of all Korea, destroyed rural communities, and enlisted Korean landowners as agents of the Japanese Government. In addition, Japanese themselves went to Korea and became landowners directly (Table 8). In India, the English destroyed the rural communities and developed a landowner system, but they didn't themselves becom landowners. The Japanese, on the other hand, by becoming landowners in Korea, exercised a much more direct and stricter control over it.

The Japanese Government tried hard to develop the production of rice in Korea, and Korean and Japanese landowners took rice in lieu of high rents from Korean tenant farmers and exported the rice to Japan. The Korean consumption of rice decreased, because Koreans were forced by high rents to eat cheap millet imported from northeast China (Table 9).

I have briefly covered the growth of world capitalism, but I would now like to look at it in more detail, especially from the point of view of the development of the squire monarchy. All countries which passed through

77

Table 9 KOREAN PRODUCTION, EXPORT, AND CONSUMPTION OF RICE, 1912-1930

(1 koku=150kg)

Year	Production	Export to Japan	Korean Per Capita Consumption	Japanese Per Capita Consumption
	1,000 koku	1,000 koku	koku	koku
1912	11,563	2,910	0.7724	1.068
1915	14,130	2,058	0.7376	1.111
1917	13,933	1,296	0.7200	1.126
1919	15,294	2,874	0.7249	1.124
1920	12,708	1.750	0.6301	1.118
1921	14,882	3,080	0.6749	1.153
1922	14,324	3,316	0.6340	1.100
1923	15,014	3,624	0.6473	1.153
1924	15,174	4,722	0.6032	1.122
1925	13,219	4,619	0.5186	1.128
1926	14,773	5,429	0.5325	1.131
1927	15,300	6.136	0.5245	1.095
1928	17,208	7,405	0.5402	1.129
1929	13,511	5,609	0.4462	1.110
1930	13,511	5,426	0.4508	1.077

Source : Chosen Beikoku Yoran (Yearbook of Rice in Korea), 1937, 3, 147.

feudal societies had squire monarchies. The French Revolution of 1789 has been called a kind of "peasant revolution," because the landowners made some concessions to the demands of the farmers. The French landowners and bourgeoisie depended on farmer support to defeat the powerful French feudal lords, who had sympathetic foreign connections. In the revolutionary parliament, lands were clearly divided between feudal lords and landowners, and efforts were made to abolish the former while keeping the latter. Just as in the English Revolution

(Civil War), the rights of the landowners were maintained.

The French absolute monarchy was strongly affected by the English industrial revolution. In order to exclude English economic control, the French monarchy tried to bring about an industrial revolution on the English model. They tried to introduce the English industrial revolution to France but the attempt was thwarted by the French Revolution. After the revolution the squire monarchy took control in France and began to implement the policy more positively; for example, the establishment of credit institutions, the construction of railways, etc. As a result the industrial revolution was achieved in about 1860, before the squire monarchy came to an end in 1870.

Germany was less advanced than France. The first moves towards an industrial revolution began at the end of the eighteenth century, as in France, but were strongly encouraged by the absolute monarchy. As I've said, under an absolute monarch the rich merchants and landowners could only develop within the limits of feudal society. The German absolute monarchy made more positive efforts to introduce industrialization than its French equivalent. It not only helped with the establishment of credit institutions and the construction of railways, but also directly built national model factories and sold them to private entrepreneurs. This did not happen in France. But despite the efforts of the absolute monarchy to limit the development of the bourgeoisie within feudal society, they finally succeeded in overthrowing that society in the March Revolution of 1848.

At that time in Germany there were already many factories that predated the revolution. In consequence there were many industrial laborers, and the German bourgeoisie needed the support of feudal power to control them. The feudal lords were not excluded by the March Revolution and could choose to become owners or capi-

79

talist farmers, with many feudal privileges. After the revolution in Germany, the squire monarchy also began,
but the German bourgeoisie were bedfellows of landowners and capitalist farmers with many feudal privileges,
and both classes closely controlled the industrial and agricultural laborers. The German industrial revolution was
completed in the second half of the nineteenth century.
The defeat of Germany in the First World War in 1918
marked the end of the squire monarchy and a proper
capitalistic society began.

Japan was further behind than Germany. In Japan the
absolute monarchy was overthrown by the impact of
world capitalism, because Japanese landowners and merchants were not well developed enough to overthrow it by
themselves. Nevertheless, the Meiji Restoration was not
without elements of the bourgeois revolution.

After the Meiji Restoration, a squire monarchy also
appeared in Japan. Until the eighteenth century, the
landowning system wasn't developed enough to overthrow
the absolute monarchy, but after the opening of the country it quickly developed (especially after the Meiji Restoration) and until about 1885, 90 percent of the national
finance was dependent upon land tax. Following the example of the English industrial revolution, the Japanese
Government tried to develop a mechanized factory system
to combat the control of world capitalism. The government concentrated on building model factories which
were then sold to private enterprise (as in Germany).
The landowners monopolized the rights to elect and become members of the parliament established in 1890 : the
right to vote was limited to landowners who had more
than twenty-five hectares of land and were over twenty-
five years of age. The right to become a member was
limited to those over thirty years of age with the same
amount of land. The Japanese industrial revolution took
place from the end of the nineteenth century.

As the industrial revolution developed, the industrial

capitalists gained more and more political power and wrested the monopoly from the hands of the landowners. Nevertheless, the close relationship between landowners and industrial capitalists continued for a long time.

The most important source of capital for the industrial capitalists was still the high rents which the landowners received from the tenant farmers, and the most profitable use for this money was still investment in industry and land. The tenant farmers, however, could barely pay the high land rents through agriculture or sericulture even when their earnings were supplemented by the wages of their daughters working in factories, mostly cotton-spinning factories. After working just a few years in the factories, many women became ill with consumption and returned home to the country only to die in the prime of life. Their wages were kept low because they had no choice but to work in view of the miserable lot of their parents, who had to pay exorbitant rents. Thus the landowners could get high rents and profitable investment from the industrial capitalists, while the industrial capitalists could get capital and a constant supply of cheap labor from the landowners.

But during the economic depression after the First World War, especially during the world economic crisis after 1919, the relationship between the two classes gradually weakened. At that time almost all Japanese were impoverished farmers and laborers. After the First World War, tenancy and labor disputes became more common. But as the market in Japan was very limited, the industrial capitalists were forced to export their goods to Korea and China, and thereby destroy industries in both countries. This led to racial problems in both countries, especially in China, and ultimately to a fifteen-year war against China that grew into the Second World War.

After the defeat in the Second World War, the occupying armies forced land reform on Japan, and as a result Japanese landowners lost political power, and the political

TABLE 10 INDUSTRIAL PRODUCTION OF SELECTED
COUNTRIES AS PERCENT OF WORLD
TOTAL, 1820-1913
(%)

Year	England	France	U. S. A.	Germany	Russia	Japan
1820	50	20	10	8	1	—
1830	—	14	—	—	—	—
1840	45	13	11	12	—	—
1850	39	10	15	15	—	—
1860	36	12	17	16	4	—
1870	32	10	23	13	4	—
1880	28	9	28	13	3	—
1890	22	8	31	14	3	—
1900	18	7	31	16	6	1
1910	14	7	35	16	5	1
1913	14	6	36	16	6	1

Source : J. Kuczinski, 1967, S. 19.

TABLE 11 BREAKDOWN OF ENGLISH COTTON TEXTILE
EXPORTS BY COUNTRY, 1820-80
(%)

Year	Europe	Turkey, Egypt, Africa	America (except U. S. A.)	U. S. A.	India	China, Indonesia, etc.	Others
1820	51	4	22	10	—	—	8
1850	16	14	27	8	23	8	4
1880	8	13	15	2	40	14	8

Source : C. P. Kinderberger, 1964, 273.

situation became the monopoly of the industrial capitalists, within, of course, the limits of American global policy. It can be said, therefore, that the Japanese squire
monarchy lasted for seventy-seven years, from the Meiji
Restoration (1868) to defeat in the Second World War

Table 12 PRODUCTION, IMPORT, EXPORT, AND
CONSUMPTION OF COTTON YARN IN
JAPAN, 1889-1900

(unit *kori*=180kg)

	Production	Import	Export	Consumption
1889	67,046	142,703	31	209,749
90	104,839	106,361	108	211,169
91	144,980	57,792	109	202,664
92	204,950	81,028	1,053	285,869
93	214,758	64,684	11,796	278,389
94	294,400	53,143	11,776	333,747
95	366,689	48,637	11,776	403,550
96	401,614	66,713	43,249	425,078
97	511,236	53,636	140,116	424,756
98	644,504	53,099	229,445	468,158
99	757,315	27,369	341,202	443,482
1900	645,432	30,170	208,732	466,870

Source : Y. Ando, 1975, 77.

(1945).

I would like to refer once more to the high land rents in India and Japan. Why could Japanese and Indian tenant farmers pay the high land rents ? The basic reason was the high agricultural productivity achieved by the intensive labor characterisic of hoeing-type agriculture. It made the development of large capitalistic farms difficult, and small family farms developed.

In France, Germany, the United States, and Japan, the industrial revolution followed the English model, and world capitalism with England at the center was destroyed by two of those countries : between 1890, the United States outstripped England in industrial production, and between 1900 and 1910 Germany outstripped England, and these countries each became centers of world capitalism (Table 10).

Export markets were slowly taken from England, and she was forced to look elsewhere. For example, 51 percent of English cotton goods were exported to European countries in 1820, but in 1880 exports to those countries had dropped to 8 percent, and exports to India had risen to 40 percent, to America (excluding the United States) to 15 percent, and to China, Indonesia, etc. to 14 percent (Table 11, 12). France, Germany, the United States, and Japan competed for these markets, and finally transformed them into colonies — the surest way of excluding competition.

NINE

Rural Community and the Relation Between Capitalism and Labor

In Chapters 7 and 8, I described how in England, Germany, France and Japan capitalism developed from the domestic industries in the villages. As there was a very close relationship between village industry and the rural community, capitalism in each country was obviously affected by the character of its rural communities. As I have mentioned, the character of labor in fallow-type agriculture is more independent and individualistic than in hoeing-type agriculture. In England, this characteristic carried over into the relationship between capital and labor. The particular skill of each artisan became of less importance as the machine developed. The private negotiation between employer and employee became public through the medium of the machine, and the relationship between capital and labor became consolidated and standardized through the bargaining right of labor. In addition, the number of industrial laborers increased rapidly as the factories developed, and the agreement between capital and labor became more standardized : the same wage for the same work. Out of this situation the trade union system developed in order to standardize and regulate working conditions. As a result, a solid standardized system in which the same wage was paid for the same job spread throughout British industry and became a feature of trade unionism. But we shouldn't only look at British trade unionism. In Japan the same process of mechanization and industrialization has produced quite a different union system.

During the Japanese industrial revolution, relations between capital and labor in factories developed along the lines of a paternal or family system. This seems to have resulted from the traditional family system in Japan, in keeping with a hoeing-type agricultural society. But at the beginning of this century, the development of the factory system demanded in Japan as well more than the private skills of traditional artisans, and systematic industrial training began. Factory work was divided according to task, and there was a slow progression from simple to more complex work. But in Japan this process took a long time. For example, in Europe, a member of a craft union could become an independent artisan after an apprenticeship of three to five years. But in Japan the length of experience and training was more important. This, combined with the family system, led to the establishment of the system of promotion through experience. That system was one characteristic of the relationship between capital and labor.

The most characteristic features the paternalistic relationship between Japanese capitalists and labor are the system of seniority-based promotion and the lifetime employment system (today the mandatory retirement age is fifty-five in most Japanese companies). Both systems began to develop early in this century and are now widespread in Japanese industry. In a capitalistic society, the wage of a worker should be decided according to his ability. In the United States, for example, salary is not based on seniority or age. But in Japan salary bears little relation to ability and is decided uniformly by seniority or age. Most Japanese think that deciding salary by ability would lead to increased competitiveness and efficiency, but they also believe that it would lead to considerable personal difficulties and that maintaining intracompany harmony would be much more difficult.

Harmony is thought to be more important than increased productivity. This is why promotion in Japanese companies is according to seniority only.

Japanese also deem it desirable for an employee to remain with a company until he reaches the retirement age. The person who changes jobs often is suspect. Likewise the company will not discharge an employee before the retirement age unless he does something illegal. In the United States, on the other hand, if a person continues to work for the same company, he is thought to lack ability. It is obvious, therefore, why Japanese workers have a strong loyalty to their company. The relationship between a company president and his workers is similar to that between a feudal lord and his vassals in the Tokugawa Period. Even if a crime is committed, it is kept within the company. If an employee discloses the crime, he becomes the object of very strong intracompany criticism. For example, the Nihon Chisso company released mercury into the Ariake Sea for a long time, and as a result many people became victims of *minamatabyō*, but no company member let the secret out. On the contrary, they aggressively tuned away from their company *minamatabyō* patients. This indicates both their loyalty to their company and at the same time their egoism (their absolute indifference to the world outside the company). Finally the cause of *minamatabyō* was discovered by research workers at the Department of Medical Science of Kumamoto University, located near the Ariake Sea, and by a doctor who had retired from Nihon Chisso.

The origins of the relations between capitalists and labor in present-day Japan clearly lie in the rural communities of the Tokugawa Period. A village functioned as an administative unit ruled by a feudal lord, and at the same time it was the focal point of its inhabitant's lives. There were many human relationships in the village : for exmple, the relationship between *honke* (the head family) and *bunke* (the branch family), between *honbyakushō*

87

(independent farmers) and *genin* (dependent farmers). *Honke* created *bunke* through the division of land between brothers, and *honke* and *bunke* banded together to form a strong group. At festival meetings *honke* members sat in the higher positions and *bunke* members in the lower positions. In the Tokugawa Period, agriculture was basically carried out by a single family, but the transplanting of rice and other major tasks were multifamily endeavors. At such times *honke* lands received priority, and *bunke* members assisted the *honke*. *Bunke* members could not work in their own fields until after the completion of work in *honke* fields.

In a village there were many *honbyakushō* and *genin*. A *honbyakushō* cultivated about one hectare of land and was a taxpayer. *Genin* and their families received food and clothing in return for working in the fields of *honbyakushō*.

In the village there were other groupings. There were many *kumi* (associations), such as the *kodomo-kumi* (children's association), *wakamono-kumi* (young people's association), and *rōjinkumi* (senior citizen's association). There were also many *kō* (fraternities), such as the Fuji kō (Fuji Fraternity) and Ise kō (Ise Fraternity). Kō were religious, economic, and social in nature. Kumi and kō were the bases of the cooperative village labor groups, which dug channels around paddy fields, repaired roads and bridges, etc.

The village functioned as a collective unit, just like a family. The feudal lord did not impose taxes directly upon each villager, but on the village itself. A village master gathered the taxes and paid them to the feudal lord. Because the village existed as a unit, villagers were egoistic. For example, when the rice crop was blighted by disease, villagers attributed the disease to certain insects, and endeavored to drive them to the next village. They thought only of saving their rice crop; they gave no thought to the next village, just as employees of Nihon Chisso gave no thought to society as a whole.

FIG. 23. ENGLISH VILLAGE IN THE MEDIEVAL ERA

Source : C. S. &C. S. Orwin 1954. Plate 22, 25.

This egoism became politically concentrated in the *tennō-sei* (emperor system). In 1871 the Japanese Government promulgated the Gōsha Teisoku (Gōsha Regulation), which stipulated that all Japanese were *ujiko* (parishioners) of a *gōsha*, the local shrine. If there were two or three shrines in a locality, and a person became a parishioner of one, he automatically became a parishioner of another under the double-*ujiko* system. The Government made Ise Shrine the chief *gōsha*. Amaterasu Ōmikami, the deity enshrined there, was the tutelary deity of the emperor. Under a broad interpretation of the double-*ujiko* system, all Japanese were parishioners of Ise Shrine, in other words, children of the emperor. The spirit of the *gōsha* came from the egoism of the villagers, and, similarly, the spirit of the emperor system derived from racial egoism. From 1871 to defeat in the Second World War, the Japanese Government tried to unite the people through the power of the emperor system. Despite its recent recognition of the law of international human

FIG. 24. JAPANESE VITLAGE IN THE MEDIEVAL ERA

Source : Miyazaki 1697, Vol. 1 Plate 1.

rights and of the treaty of international aid to refugees, the Government still uses racial egoism as a uniting force, which leads me to conclude that the emperor system is still influential.

In the first half of this century, the paternal relationship between capitalists and labor became more independent and individualistic in line with the development of capitalism. Japanese laborers began to become more individualistic in character. In Europe the individualistic relationship between capitalists and labor was based on the individualism of laborers.

But in Japan, before the independent self-consciousness of the laborers was fully formed, the ideology of the proletariat class based on Marxism was introduced from Europe and America, and the ideological opposition between capitalists and labor became mixed with traditional paternalism. Thus, in spite of the fact that the paternal relationship was still strong, a proletariat consciousness developed among laborers. In Japan, although the pro-letariat class did not evolve naturally from traditional human relations, it did support the Japanese trade union movement and become an important source of energy in the labor movement.

The Japanese trade union movement has two souls : the soul of the traditional family system, or paternalism, and the soul of Marxist class struggle. So there has never been a balanced relationship between capitalists and laborers. The latter are too quick to join a political movement.

TEN

The Tennō System

(1) The Ancient Tennō System

The Tennō system was created in the seventh century as a political means to establish a Japanese-style statutory nation on the model of the statutory system in China. In the seventh century the clan system was still intact and there existed a kind of totemism, specifically, each clan was believed to be desceded from a separate deity. The Ōgimi were believed to be descended from the Sun Goddess. Moreover, as a poems by Hitomaro indicates, the head of the Ōgimi was believed to be a deity, or Tennō. Seventh-century politicians had propagated that belief. The Tennō system has continued without interruption to the present day.

Takihara-miya, a branch of Ise Shrine, is dedicated to the Sun Goddess who is the ancestor of the Tennō. The shrine is a two-hour car ride west from Ise Shrine. The shrine's *koden-chi*, alternate site, is a rectangular lot in the corner of a thick forest of broad-leaved evergreens along a limpid steam. The grounds of the *koden-chi* are covered with pebbles. It is truly a refreshing place. In the *koden-chi*, in squares demarked by black stones, stand two miniature wooden houses some twenty centimeters high. Beneath the roofs of the house there are reportedly *yorishiro*, the dwelling places of deities, in the form of small sticks in the ground, though we are not allowed to them.

To the right of the *koden-chi* are the two simple build-ings of Takihara-miya. Every thirty years the shrine is pulled down and a new shrine is erected on the *yorishiro* of the *koden-chi*. Afterwards the former site of the shrine will be the *koden-chi*.

Ise Shrine is several times as large as Takihara-miya. To the right of Ise Shrine is a *koden-chi*. Though Takihara-miya is today believed to be a branch of Ise Shrine, some scholars say that Takihara-miya may be older, in other words, that the former may be the precur-sor of the latter. Whether the theory is reliable or not, there is something refreshing about the *koden-chi*, which probably represent Japanese religion in its most primitive form.

Japanese summers are especially hot and humid, and so the Japanese bathe to remove sweat and dirt. It seems the ancient Japanese thought that the soul, just like the body, became dirty. Impurities of the soul are called *kegare*. The ancients purified the soul through *mis-ogi*, ablutions in a limpid stream.

In Judaism and Christianity a sin is an act that by violating the will of God incurs his wrath, and in those religions expiation lies in confession of the sin to God and in repentance. (The Christian belief is that Christ bears the blame for the sins of man. Chapter 4, Verse 25, of The Letter of Paul to the Romans says, in part, "He was given up to death for our misdeeds and raised to life to justify us.") *Kegare*, however, is quite different from the Judeo-Christian sin. There is almost no difference be-tween the two in that *kegare* results from a disregard of the will of the deities. But unlike in Judaism and Christ-ianity, in Japanese primitive religion a sinner absolved his sin by performing *misogi* in a limpid stream, not by con-fessing his sin to the deities and repenting. According to Judaism and Christianity, it is necessary that the sinner vow never to commit the same sin again in order to receive God's pardon. (Chapter 3 of Jonah says, in part,

"They are to clothe themselves in sackcloth and call on
God with all their might. Let every man abandon his
wicked ways and his habitual violence. It may be that
God will repent and turn away from his anger ; and so
we shall not perish.") On the contrary, in Japanese religion whenever the soul is sullied it can be purified, and
the repetition of *misogi* does not diminish its power. In
other words, in Judaism and Christianity sin is closely
related to the character of the sinner, while in Japanese
primitive religion *kegare* is as impersonal as dirt on the
body.

Needless to say, the concept of *kegare* is closely related
to the natural features of Japan. For that reason, the
koden-chi of Takihara-miya is refreshing or ought to be
refreshing. That Ise Shrine appeals to the Japanese
whenever they visit it is attributable to their delight in
that which refreshes. That delight is related to the
Japanese unsurpassed fondness for bathing. This racial
feeling can probably be traced back to the time before Ise
Shrine was dedicated to the deity from whom the Tennō
is descended. It was probably necessary that the Tennō
system appeal to this racial feeling, and for that reason,
the Sun Goddess was made the ancestor of the Tennō.

According to Masaaki Ueda (1970), the original name
of Ameterasu-ōmikami, the Sun Goddess, was Ōhirumemuchi, which initially referred to the position of a
medium in the service of the Sun Goddess. In the
period before Amaterasu-ōmikami represented the Sun
Goddess, various provinces — among them, Yamashiro,
Yamato, Kawachi, Settsu, Tanba, Harima, Chikugo, and
Tsushima — as well as Ise, worshipped their own sun
goddesses. Sun-Goddess worship was very popular
among farmers. Ōhirumemuchi, who served the most
influential sun goddess, occupied the first place later as
the Tennō's ancestor, Amaterasu-ōmikami, and was
promoted to Deity Presiding Over the Plain of High
Heaven. It is conjectured that Amaterasu-ōmikami suc-

94

ceeded Takamimusubi, the Tennō's ancestor.

Takamimusubi, also known as Takagi-no-kami (Deity of Tall Trees), is the deification of the *himorogi*, a tall tree in which the deity is believed to reside. Takamimusubi is a deity closely connected with the *himorogi* used in a festival invoking the Deity of Rice Fields. Takamimusubi is evidently the Deity of Rice Fields. *Musu* means that a plant germinates by itself, and *bi* refers to the power of the soul. It was Takamimusubi that Ōhirumemuchi served as a medium. After the establishment of a connection between a sun goddess and Takamimusubi, the former came to surpass the latter. Later this sun goddess became Amaterasu-ōmikami, the Tennō's ancestor, to whom people were prohibited from making an offering, because the Tennō monopolized worship of her.

According to Keiji Iwata (1966), even today in Southeast Asia — particularly in Thailand — a tall tree is erected in a paddy before unhulled rice is sowed. The tall tree is supposed to bring a good rice crop by guiding the Spirit of Cereals to the paddy. The tall tree is probably the origin of Takagino-kami, the alternate name for Takamimusubi.

As the sun goddess identified with Amaterasu-ōmikami was monopolized exclusively by the Ōgimi, she was elevated to the Deity Presiding Over the Plain of High Heaven. The Ōgimi probably came to occupy a place of political preeminence by virtue of their monopoly of the worship of Amaterasu-ōmikami. Thus the genealogy of the deities was begun. The genealogy was completed in the *Kojiki* (Record of Ancient Matters) and the *Nihonshoki* (The Chronicles of Japan), both of which regard Amaterasu-ōmikami as Takamimusubi's descendant.

How was Takamimusubi (the Deity of Rice Fields) or Amaterasu-ōmikami (the Sun Goddess) related to the Japanese love of the purity of the soul? The livelihood of farmers is theatened by crop damage owing to blight and insects. In ancient Japan, it was probably impossible to contain such damage once it had begun. During the Edo Period (1603 – 1867) each village performed a ceremony called *mushiokuri*, in which insects were driven away by ringing gongs and beating drums. The ceremony is still performed in Kamihinozawa, Minano Town, in the Chichibu Basin of Saitama Prefecture. Here is a description :

"Every August 17 more than thirty of the households in the community participate in *mushiokuri*. The day is called Bongara, the day after *kyū-bon*. which is the day corresponding to *o-bon* in the following month. The community performs *hotokeokuri*, the ceremony of seeing off souls, on the 16th. However, the souls of dead with no surviving relatives are seen off on the 17th, the same day as *mushi-okuri* ... Toward the day of the mass for the dead, the caretakers of Kōfuku Temple meet there and spend the night cutting *norose* from pieces of paper of five different colors. The norose, also known as *tare*, are exorcised at the mass on the 16th and distributed to each house during the morning of the next day, when the *mushi-okuri* is held. In the morning, each household brings from the mountains small bamboo plants, about six inches long and as thick as the forefinger, and cuts off their ends, ensuring that two or three sections with branches remain, to be used as *okuri-take*. Norose are hung on the okuri-itake. In addition, *iri-sago* (parched barley, beans, foxtail millet, etc.), each of which is enclosed in a piece of twisted paper, are hung on them ... Insects are not only harmful to crops, but are also believed to evil spirits lurking in the body. The iri-sago serve to expel insects from houses. Around three o'clock in the afternoon, children carrying okuri-take meet at a mountain spring ... They are accompanied by adults playing different kinds of drums and flutes. After the leader chants *onbēfuri*,the children begin shouting *nāni mushō okuruyō* in unison and start to march along mountain paths through odiferous grasses. The opposite mountain echoes their voices calling for the seeing off of every insect." (From *Chichibu — Matsuri to Minkan Shinkō* [Chichibu — Festival and Folk Faith], by Seiichirō Asami)

The last part of "Rokugatsu no Misoka no Ōharai" (The Exorcism on the Last Day of June), which is representative of the Shinto prayers to be recited to the deities for the purpose of removing *kegare*, says that various *kegare* have been blown out to sea, just like a big ship is, and destroyed, and that henceforth there was no more *kegare* in the world. The prayer was read on the last days of June and December during events held to eliminate all *kegare*. While in Judaism and Christianity expiation is granted on the condition that a person never repeats the sin, in Japanese primitive religion *kegare* are regularly removed, as dirt, which collects on the body because of the heat and humidity, is washed off heat and humidity, is washed off by periodic bathing. The Japanese idea of *kegare* is very close to the spirit behind *mushi-okuri*.

I am unable, of course, to tell when *mushi-okuri* began. However, if the ceremony is as old as damage to crops from blight and insects, the farmers' worship of the Sun Goddess can easily be connected with the ceremony to remove *kegare*. Therefore, the clan able to monopolize Amaterasu-ōmikami as their ancestor was able to control farmers' primitive religious feelings.

Later the character of this religious authority or charisma changed in that it became hereditary when Ōkimi, the leader of the ancient Yamato dynasty, finally became the Tennō, the supreme leader of the statutory nation based on the Tennō system. The right of heredity was guaranteed by the fact that the successor was descended from Amatersu-ōmikami and his possession of the Three Sacred Treasures of the Imperial House to prove his lineage.

(2) The Medieval Tennō System

After the Taika Reforms (645), it seems the Tennō was the ruler occupying the highest position in the political system that was a monarchy in both name and reality, a reality in accordance with the statutory system. However, during the Monarch Age the ancient Tennō system was gradually replaced by a new system. During that age the Tennō was deprived of his political power and reduced to a nominal ruler, despite his holding the highest position in the political system, in other words, in the statutory system. The position of Tennō changed from one who rules to one who is ruled, or from one who uses others to one who is used. However, it is perhaps possible that the loss of political power enabled the Tennō to live peaceably, free of violent domination.

When Minamoto Yoritomo established the headquarters of his military government in Kamakura after his clan defeated the Taira, the ancient Tennō system came to an end in both name and reality. The samurai definitely divested the Tennō of political power, which actually weakened the nominal Tennō system, confined him Kyōto, and established their headquarters in a distant place to exclude him from political power. Against that background the medieval Tennō system was completed. It was the medieval Tennō system that gave the Tennō system the symbolic character it retains today. In other words, the Tennō was no longer a ruler but a symbolic religious figure. As the Tennō was a superior being, he was kept isolated from common people and deified. The religious authority of the Tennō, who was deified in spite of his human attributes, was used to control the people's religious sentiments. Whether in the West or in Japan, the double structure of feudalism — the coexistence of centralization and decentralization or to be more exact, centralization in name and decentralization in relity — required the separation of power and authority.

The relationship between a monarch or emperor and the pope in the West was one example. As for Japan, the Tennō was regarded as the most suitable symbol for making the decentralized power as authoritative as centralized power, because in the medievel age there was no other clan with mythological or legendary origins more familiar than those of the Tennō clan. But it had to be kept in mind aways that the Tennō was not a power but a political tool. In other words, the Tennō was regarded as a crown or a sacred treasure the person in power sought to possess in order to validate his rule. Consequently, it was a top priority of the ruler to control Kyōto and the Tennō. The person who controlled the Tennō was believed to control the entire nation.

Nevertheless, after assuming power, the ruler began to feel that the Tennō, of whom he had taken advantage, was a nuisance. The Tennō was not a crown to be worn, and quite naturally, sometimes desired power. While using the Tennō, the ruler had to prevent him from coming into power and prevent others from using him. So the ruler worked to keep the Tennō in isolation as well as to deify him.

In moden times the Tokugawa Shogunate understood well that it must use the Tennō while preventing others from using him. However, it was difficult to deny others access to the Tennō, owing to the double structure of feudalism. Therefore, the Shogunate used political artifice to keep the Tennō in isolation and prevent him from coming into power. The deification of the Tennō was perfected. Books by Western sojourners to Japan during the Edo Period (1603 - 1867) reveal how the Japanese typically felt about the Tennō. An example is *The Annals of the Great Japanese Empire*, 1645, by François Caron (1600-1673), which greatly helped Westerners to understand Japan. Caron resided as many as twenty-three years in Japan, working for the Dutch factory in Hirado as an interpreter and later managing it. He had a good command of Japanese and loved Japan. He and his Japanese wife had six children. Translated into English, German, and French, *The Annals of the Great Japanese Empire* was read by many Westerners.

Caron wrote that the supreme ruler of Japan was called the Tycoon and that he dominated a number of feudal lords. The capital, Edo, was a great city with a large castle in which lived the Tycoon. In addition to the Tycoon, there was the Tennō in Kyōto, the former capital. The Tennō, previously the supreme ruler, exercised power over everything but politics and performed innumerable ceremonies in a solemn, formal manner throughout the year.

Later other Westerners noted the peculiar double structure of the Japanese political system. Here is how Sir Rutherford Alcock described it in *The Capital of the Tycoon : A Narrative of a Three Years' Residence in Japan,* 1863 : "This double machinery of a titular Sovereign who only reigns, and a Lieutenant of the empire who only governs, and does not reign, from generation to generation is certainly something very curious." He describes the Tennō (here Mikado) as follows : "The Mikado of the day is the exact type of the last descendant of Clovis, sitting 'sad and solitary, effeminate and degenerate,' doomed only to wield 'a barren sceptre,' and sigh away a burdensome and useless existence of mock pageantry ; — never permitted to pass the gates of his prison-palace."

Also, Caron comments as follows about the Tennō : "According to Japaness documents, Japan had been governed by the hereditary sovereign called Tennō from ancient times until one hundred years ago. The people respect him as their leader and deify him as well. Therefore, none have attempted rebellion against him. They believe the Tennō is sacred, and that opposing him would be equivalent to opposing deities ... Since the Tennō is deified, he does not walk on the ground, dwarfs the sun and moon, and does not cut his hair or nails no matter how long they grow. Each of his meals is prepared with new pots. He has twelve wives. Various ceremonies are performed when a woman becomes the wife of the Tennō. When the Tennō goes out, each wife accompanies him in an oxcart indicating her family crest and title. In the palace are two rows of six houses each. The family crest and title of each resident appears on her house. The wives live with their maids in the houses. In addition, there are houses for court ladies. Since there is no way of ascertaining which of the twelve houses the Tennō will visit, every evening the wives prepare a banquet and have musicians stand by in anticipation. Upon learning which house he has visited, the eleven other wives will have the meals carried to the house and proceed there with their maids and musicians in order to assist the wife who has had the honor of the visit and entertain him as much as possible by staging a musical comedy or the like." (From *The Annals of the Great Japanese Empire*)

Caron's image of the Tennō probably corresponded to the contemporary popular image of him. The quotation indicates well the apotheosis and isolation of the Tennō.

(3) The Modern Tennō System

THE modern Tennō system incorporates authority and power, which had been separated in name and reality since the establishment of the Kamakura Shogunate. An ideological revolution was the major factor behind the incorporation. The ideological roots of the modern Tennō system are in the Mito school of politics and history, and in the study of Japanes classic literature. Shōin Yoshida (1830 - 59), who was influenced by the Mito school, greatly contributed to the modern Tennō system by establishing the theory that the whole nation belongs to the Tennō. That was an idea not found in the classics.

The visit to Japan by Commodore Perry in 1853 made

Shōin reappraise his views about the Tennō. The Mito school and Utsunomiya Mokurin had opened Shōin's eyes to the Tennō. Seishisai Aizawa, a representative thinker of the Mito school, observed in *Shinron* the following about the Tennō-Shogun relationship :

"The Shogun governs the nation under the authority of the Tennō. Each feudal lord governs his domain, and maintains peace and order for the people. We serve the Tennō and his ancestors by conforming to the ways of our daimyos and Shogunate."

The letter Shōin wrote his elder brother in 1855 says in part : "Fealty to the Shogun is identical with fealty to the Tennō." Nevertheless, he later began to doubt if he was right. He was inclined to value fealy to the Tennō above that to the Shogun. That was because he never succeeded in altering the opinions of the Shogunate and his domain regarding how they should cope with the turbulent political situation in the closing years of the Shogunate. The letter he wrote in 1856, while in prison, to Mokurin indicates his thinking at the time :

"Since I am a subject of the Mōri family, day and night I devote myself to serving them. The Mōri are subjects of the Tennō, and so I am serving the Tennō day and night. Fealty to a daimyo can be regarded as fealty to the Tennō. The Mōri, however, have neglected their duties as the Tennō's subjects for six hundred years ... I think now is the time for the Mōri to compensate for their six hundred years of continuous negligence."

The following is quoted from *Heishin Yūshitsu Bunko*, written by Shōin in 1856.

"Their loyalty to the Tennō leads some to indignation against barbarians [foreigners], while others have become supporters of the Tennō because of their indignation against the barbarians. I devoted myself in childhood to the teachings of my family, and I taught military science. Thereby, I came to learn that the barbarians deserve our contempt. Later I thought about why Japan was infested with barbarians, and understood why the nation was declining. I also learned that the situation behind the Tennō is quite serious. However, I was unable to decide whether we ought to serve the Tennō out of loyalty or out of indignation against the barbarians. I did not know which was the proper motive until I received enlightenment from a friend over a period of eight months. Uutil then it had seemed that indignation against the barbarians would instill in the people loyalty to the Tennō. I found that I had been mistaken, and that those who serve the Tennō out of indignation against the barbarians should not be regarded as loyalists."

Shōin regretted that pressure from the Western powers had made him realize the true raison d'etre of the Tennō. He reconsidered the Tennō's role in history and concluded that all Japanese were the Tennō's subjects.

The theory that all Japaness were the Tennō's subjects became the unshakable principle of Shōin's ideology, and spurred Shōin to lead partisans in an attempt to overthrow the Tokugawa Shogunate. We can trace the development of his ideology in the many letters he addressed to his disciples in the several months before his execution in 1859. He recognized that the line of descent in the Imperial Family had remained unbroken for centuries, and believed the whole nation owed fealty to the Tennō, the supreme ruler, since it had benefited from his benevolence. The theory that all Japanese are subjects of the Tennō, a theory Shōin formulated after struggling with the problem of the Tennō-Shogun relation, was adopted by his disciples after his death and drawn upon during the establishment of the Meiji Government, which marked the start of the modern political system.

I would like to add something to the general view that the national state was established by the Meiji Government. First of all, national state means centralized state. G. R. Elton says that the establishment of an absolute dynasty in Britain should be regarded as the establish-

103

ment of a centralized, monarchic, national state. In the case of Japan, it is generally accepted that the Meiji Government established a national state. The truth, however, is that the Tokugawa Shogunate established the centralized, monarchic, national state to which Elton refers, because the Tokugawa shoguns were regarded as emperors, or tycoons, by contemporary Westerners. A national state had already been established in Japan in the seventeenth century. The Meiji Government did not establish a national state, but shifted the system of the national state from feudalism to capitalism. The Meiji Government had to unite authority and power, separated during the centuries since the Kamakura Period, in order to imitate political systems of Western countries. That is why the ancient Tennō system, in which authority and power were united, was revived. Government leaders chose to incorporate power (Tycoon) into authority (Tennō), while power incorporated authoriy in Westen countries. The revival of the ancient Tennō system brought about the revival of the statutory system, which had been reduced to a titular system for one thousand years.

How did the Meiji Government embody the theory that the whole nation belonged to the Tennō ? It established a system of national Shintoism with the Tennō as the central figure. The Government began by founding in 1868, the first year of Meiji, a bureau to supervise shrines throughout the country. The Government began to separate Shintoism and Buddhism with the object of purifying and elevating the former. A result of the Goverment action was a nationwide anti-Buddhist movement. The common on people, whose religious beliefs and sentiments were rooted in a mixture of Buddhism and Shitoism, bridled at the dogmatic anti-Buddhism. Miyata Noboru describes their reaction in *Iki-gami Shinkō* (Faith in Living Deities) : "The public were upset and came to join fraternities headed by lower-class religionists advocating a mixture of Buddhism and Shintoism. The fraternities were organized in succession …

"Next the Government launched a program of shrine construction in hope of consolidating faith in the Tennō. The Kyōto Chūkon Shrine, dedicated to those killed in the fighting leading to the Meiji Restoration, was moved to Tōkyō and renamed Tōkyō Shōkonsha (now Yasukuni Shrine). The Government founded shrines for those who had made noteworthy contributions to former Tennōs, as well as for former Tennōs and princes."

The Government intended to establish a Tennō theology and consolidate it by incorporating the faith of the masses. The system of ranking shrines was aimed at the consolidation of a Tennō theology. Again I quote from *Iki-gami Shinkō* :

"The system of ranking shrines was established in 1871. In the system *kanpei* shrines, shrines which received offerings from the Imperial Household, were ranked first, followed by semi-kanpeishrines ; national shrines, among which are the popular Kumano, Konpira, and Togakushi Shrines : prefectural shrines ; county shrines ; and village shrines. It is evident that the Meiji Government intended to bring the common people, whose faith took the form of shrine worship, under it control and to use the national conception of deity for political purposes. That is the reason the Government created a system of ranking shrines in which those dedicated to former Tennōs and their loyal subjects were preeminent."

Toward the end of the Meiji Era, the Government began a program to rapidly construct shrines in villages across the country. By the time each village had its own shrine, nearly all the measures for the promotion of Tennō theology had been taken. Thus the Meiji Government popularized Tennō theology, thereby succeeding in the systemization and justification of the theory that all Japanese are the Tennō's subjects. That was how the modern Tennō system was completed.

Part II

Aspects of Japanese Agriculture

ONE

Did the Agricultural Revolution take place in Japan ?

Many Japanese scholars say that an agricultural revolution did not take place in Japan, and that this fact
itself is the feature of Japanese agriculture. In my opion,
if the changes in English agriculture in the 18th and 19th
centuries can be called an agricultural revolution, the
changes of that occurred in Japanese agriculture in the
19th and 20th centuries can also be called an agricultural
revolution.

In Part I Chapter 2, I divided the grain farming of the
world into fallow-type and hoeing-type, and maintained
that the character of labor in fallow-type agriclture and in
hoeing-type agriculture tends to be different, that is, labor
in fallow-type agriculture tends to become extensive,
whereas labor in hoeing-type agriculture tends to become
intensive. Therefore, in the modernization of agriculture,
saved labor is used to enlarge the area under cultivation,
and there is no intensification of labor on the same place
of land. In hoeing-type agriculture, however, the area
under cultivation tends to remain the same, and the intensity of work increases to the detriment of crop yield.

However, in special instances like the industrial revolution, when a rapid increase in agricultural production is
made necessary to meet the rapid increase of non-agri-
cultural population, a new technique opposed to the original techniques is introduced to the old husbandry system.

Fig. 25. CHARLES TOWNSHEND

Source : Franklin 1948, 123.

The English agricultural revolution took place in the 18th and 19th centuries in this way. Of course, English agriculture had developed before that time. Originally there no excellent fodders in England. Farmers bred their cattle on very little grass in meadows. Their cattle was very few, and manure was also very scarce, and subsequently their agricultural production was very low.

In the 17th century, excellent types of grasses (for example, red clover, lucern, etc.) were introduced from the low countries in Europe to England. As a result, cattle and manure increased. But it was possible to cultivate the new types of grasses though the field system was not changed. The change of agriculture in the 18th and 19th centuries was a quite different story from the introduction of red clovers etc. At that time, agricultural production rapidly promoted the dissemination of Norfolk husbandry to satisfy the larger demand created by the

FIG. 26. TOWNSHEND'S HOUSE AND FARM ON RENHOM IN NORFOLK

1.

2.

3.

1. Gate 2. House 3. Farm
Source : the author

111

Fig. 27 THOMAS WILLIAM COKE

Source : C. S. Orwin 1949, Plote 1.

industrial revolution. The English agricultural revolution was largely dependent on the shift from the garden to field type turnip cultivation. Originally, the turnip was cultivated as garden vegetable, but in the 18th and 19th centuries farmers began to plant turnips in fields as fodder. The increased production of fodder boosted the livestock production, which, in turn, produced more manure. The increase in manure improved the agricultural yield.

English agriculture is of the fallow-type; hoeing is unnecessary. But gardening requires hoeing even in fallow-type agriculture. Turnip, being a garden crop, requires hoeing. At the beginning of the 18th century, turnips were first cultivated as fodder in the sandy soil of Norfolk. The typical plot was two or three acres, and even the largest did not exceed twenty acres, because turnips required hand hoeing. It was Charles Townshend (1674–1738) who began the cultivation of turnips in a Norfolk

112

Fig. 28. COKE'S HOUSE ON HOLKHAM IN NORFOLK

1.

2.

1. Gate   2. The Holkham Monument
Source : the author

field. Little is known about him except that he mixed turnips with wheat, barley, and clover in a field of a few hundred acres, and created Norfolk husbandry, which was based on the rotation of four crops (wheat → turnip → barley → clover) (Fig. 25, 26).

He seems to have hoed many acres of turnips by hand, following the gardening method. Because it was such hard work, Norfolk husbandry was largely confined to the sandy soil of Norfolk. It was William Coke (1752-1842) (Fig. 27, 28) who made the large-scale cultivation of tur-

FIG. 29. THE DRILL INVENTED BY J. TULL

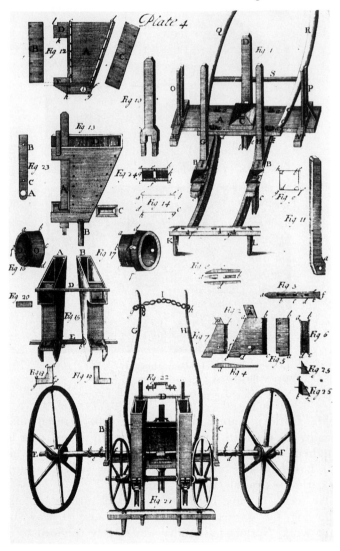

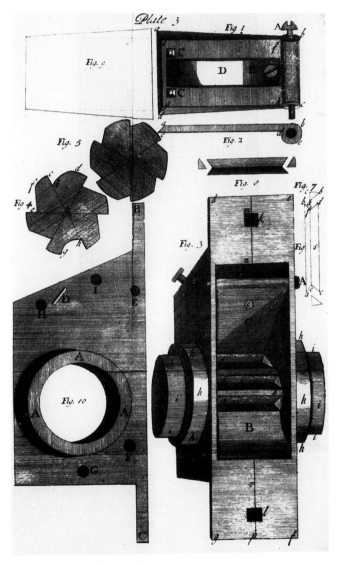

Source : Tull 1733, Plate 3, 4.

115

Fig. 30. JETHRO TULL

Source : J. A. Widtsoe 1919, Plate 1.

nips possible by the horse drill invented by J. Tull (Fig. 29, 30). If farmers used a horse drill to sow the seeds, subsequent hoeing could be done with a plough. After this innovation, the field cultivation of turnips spread in the first half of the 19th century.

Fallow-type agriculture traditionally depended on extensive rather than intensive labor, such as hoeing. When a rapid increase in agricultural production was made necessary by the industrial revolution, turnip cultivation moved from the garden to the field. But, in so far as hoeing was manual, as it was in the garden, Norfolk remained the only site of the field cultivation of turnips. Only the introduction of mechanized techniques made possible the field cultivation of turnips on a large scale. These mechanized techniques were in the fallow-type agriculture tradition.

The English traditional field system had been in the tradition of the three-field system for a long time. The cultivation of red clovers was possible under the three-field system, but the cultivation of turnips was not. If farmers wished to cultivate turnips, they had to destroy the old three field system and enclose these peices of fields. However, the farmers could not destroy the old system and construct the fields individually. That is, almost all the farmers in a village had to do it at the same time. Therefore, the English Government passed the enclosure acts in the 18th and 19th centuries, and if beyond two-thirds of the land owners of a village approved of a plan of enclosure, allowed to enclose all the fields of a village.

In Japan also, the deep tillage of rice paddy fields changed from hoeing by hand to ploughing by cattle along with the industrial revolution, in the 19th and 20th centuries. The Japanese plough was originally introduced from North China by way of Korea in the 7th century, and was used by Japanese farmers until the beginning of this century. This plough was invented in North China. As North China is a dry zone, this plough was of the D (dry zone) -type, designed for shallow tillage. But as Japan is in the humid zone, the H (humid zone) -type plough was more suitable. Why was the D-type plough used for so long in Japan?

I think there are several reasons. Chinese culture deeply influenced Japan, and the long-sole Chinese plough was suitable for making the nonosmotic base of the rice paddy field. When the industrial revolution made necessary increased agricultural production, in particular, increased rice production, the no-sole plough was adopted for the rice fields in Fukuoka.

In *Suevey of Agriculture and Fishing Implements in Fukuoka Prefecture*, 1879, reprinted in 1982 (see Appendex A), we can find the no-sole ploughs in Shima and Ito districts of Fukuoka Prefecture. These two districts were in the do-

117

Fig. 31. A MAP OF JAPAN, ESPECIALLY FUKUOKA AND TSUSHIMA

main of Tsushima island during the Tokugawa period (1603-1868). In Tsushima island, farmers tilled the fields deeply with no-sole plough already in the 17th century. In Korea, farmers used long-sole plough to till shallowly the paddy fields, and no-sole plough till deeply the fields. In Tokugawa period, Tsushima island was the only country which had trade with Korea (Fig. 31). In my opinion, the no-sole plough was brought from Korea to Tsushima island before the 17th century and from Tsushima island to its domain in Fukuoka. In the Meiji era, farmers of Fukuoka seem to have applied the deep tillage by no-sole plough to the rice paddy fields as well.

The long-sole prevented deep tillage, but the removal of the sole from the plough made deep tillage possible. This new method of rice cultivation by which the farmers of Fukuoka Prefecture began to till deeply and to spread manure using no-sole plough by cattle, the so-called Fukuoka husbandry greatly reduced the labor of deep tillage of rice fields by hand, and the saved labor was used to develop multiple and mixed farming. These intensive techniques were in the hoeing-type agricultural tradition.

From the ancient times to the 20th century, Japanese farmers kept very few cattle and had very little manure. Thir manures were mainly grasses and human manure. But Fukuoka husbandry required cattle and the diffusion of this new type of husbandry accelarated the increase of cattle and manure. On the other hand, the climate in Japan is very humid and hot in summer, and manures were brought into full play with deep tillage. In this way, the diffusion on of Fukuoka husbandry increased agricultural productivity.

Fukuoka husbandry spread rapidly all over Japan during the industrial revolution. Without a sole, however, a plough is very difficult to handle and much physical strength was required to push the no-sole plough. Japanese farmers longed for an efficient but more manageable plough. In the first half of the 20th century, such a plough was invented. It was a short-sole plough, an original Japanese H-type plough based on both the Chinese long-sole plough and no-sole plough.

In the Meiji era, almost all Japanese rice fields were irregular in shape, and very humid, and Fukuoka husbandry could not be applied to such rice fields. It was necessary to reform and drain them. At that time, the reforming and drainage of the rice fields was called the re-adjustment of rice fields. But farmers could not re-adjust them individually, it had to be done by all the farmers in a village at the same time. The Japanese Government passed the re-adjustment act in 1899, and if beyond two-thirds of land owners of a village approved of a plan of re-adjustment, it was allowd to re-adjust all the

119

rice fields of a village.

Therefore, if the Norfolk husbandry which spread in England by the enclosure acts and the resulting development of agricultural production in the 18th and 19th centuries can be called an agricultural revolution, the Fukuoka husbandry which spread in Japan by the readjustment act and the resulting rapid development of agricultural production should be named an agricultural revolution also in my opinion.

TWO

The Ne-no-hi-kara-suki of Shôsôin

(1)　The Ne-no-hi-kara-suki

The word Shôsôin meant the most important of all the storehouses belonging to each large temple of the Nara period when the capital of Japan was in Nara (710-784 A. D.), but these Shôsôins all became extinct eycept that of Tôdaiji temple, so today Shôsôin refers only to the storehouse of Tôdaiji temple.

Owing to the close connection between Tôdaiji temple and the court, there are articles in the Shôsôin which used to belong to the emperors and aristocrats of the Nara period. The permission of emperors has been needed from the Nara period to the present time to open the Shôsôin, so these articles are well preserved. Many of them were brought from various parts of Asia, especially China. Some of them have already disappeared from use in these parts, so the articles preserved in the Shôsôin provide first-class data for the study of ancient Japan as of ancient Asia, and especially China.

There are two implements named Ne-no-hi-kara-suki in the Shôsôin. In ancient Japan, there was a ceremony in the palace on the first Ne-no-hi (the day of rats, that is the first day by calculation based upon twelve kinds of animals) of the first month of the year when the emperor used the implement Kara-suki for the encouragement of agriculture and the empress used a broom to sweep the

FIG. 32.   NE-NO-HI-KARA-SUKI

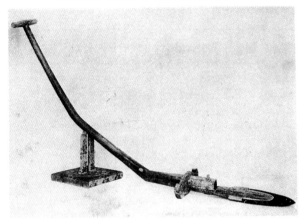

The Ne-no-hi-kara-suki as it is displayed in the Shôsôin.

silkworm room for the encouragement of sericulture. We know that Ne-no-hi-kara-suki was used by an emperor for this ceremony on January 3rd, 758 by the letters inscribed on the wooden-shaft[1].

These two implements are almost the same. As shown in Figs. 1 and 2[2] the wooden-shaft is bent at two places. The shortest distance between both ends of one is 131 cm and the actual length is 153.5 cm, and for the other 130 cm and 141 cm respectively. There is a guard where the blade is jointed to the wooden-shaft. The shaft is made of oak and the wooden-blade is of hinoki (Chamaecyparis obtusa Endl.). These wooden parts are painted all over in a pinkish colour, over which are drawn marks suggesting the grain of the wood in sapan-juice. As shown in Fig. 32[3], the iron shoe is decorated on both sides with flowering plants, butterflies and birds, in gold and silver. The white strip between the iron and the wood indicates a more recent repair[4]. From this they seem to have been used not for tilling but for the ceremony alone.

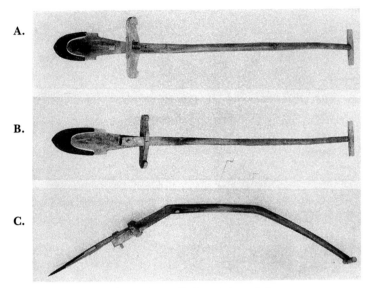

A. from the side; B. from above; C. from below of the same

(2) The Introduction of the Plough to Japan

The word *Kara* originally referred to a district in ancient South Korea which had a close connection with Japan. Later, *Kara* came to indicate Korea itself and also China. The word *Suki* means spade or plough. Therefore, *Kara-suki* meant the spade or plough introduced from Korea or China.

There are many theories concerning the date and origin of agriculture in Japan, but it has been recently recognized by many scholars that Japanese agriculture originated with rice cultivation introduced from the Yang-tsu-chiang Valley to West Japan and South Korea almost contemporaneously in the 3rd Century B. C.[5] The farming tools of Japan were at first made entirely of wood — iron tools were used only to make implements — and

123

The iron blade of the Ne-no-hi-kara-suki seen from the front (right) and from the back (left).
Source : Shôsôin 1942, Plate 1, 2, 3.

were of different types according to their purpose. From this we know that farming tools were introduced to Japan in a considerably developed form.

These wooden tools fall into two groups : one mainly used for tilling the soil, and the other mainly for stirring up the muddy soil of rice fields. The most typical tool of the former group is a hoe with a narrow mouth, of which the shaft is at an angle of 60-80°, which seems to make it possible to till the soil deeply (Fig. 33 : 1). On the other hand, the most typical tool of the latter group is a hoe with a wide mouth, of which the shaft is at an angle of 40°, which seems to make it difficult to till deeply (Fig. 33 : 2). There are also two kinds of rake-hoes. One with a shaft at an angle of 60-70° seems to be suitable for tilling the soil dceply, especially the muddy soil of rice fields, since in rice fields a common hoe is too heavy to lift

FIG. 33. EARLY WOODEN FARMING TOOLS IN JAPAN

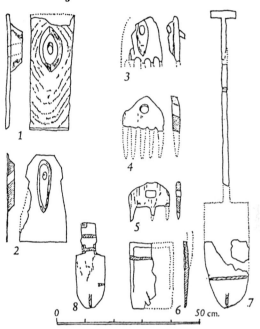

1-2 are hoes, 3-5 are rake-hoes ; 6-8 are spades. 1-3 and 6-8 were made in the first stage of the *Yayoi* period (3rd-2nd Century B. C.), and 4-5 were made in the second and third stages of that period (lst Century B. C. -3rd Century A. D.).
Source : Kinoshita 1966, 235

because the muddy soil adheres to the edge (Fig. 33 : 3, 4). The other with a shaft at an angle of 90° seems to be suitable for raking (Fig. 33 : 5). There are various kinds of spades : one is suitable for digging and carrying off the soil (Fig. 33 : 6), another is suitable for tilling the soil (Fig. 33 : 7), and the third is especially suitable for digging small holes in the soil (Fig. 33 : 8)[6]. Tillage by these tools of the first group sems to have been practised

125

FIG. 34   EARLY IRON HOES AND IRON HOES OR SPADES IN JAPAN

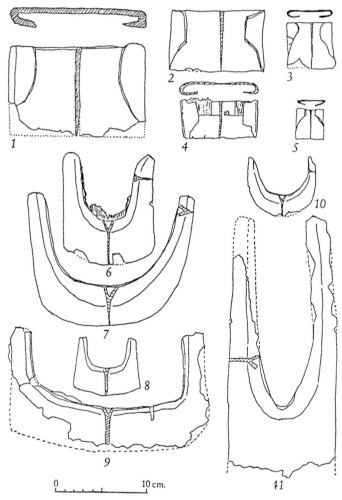

1-5 are early iron hoes, and 6-11 are iron hoes or spades with U-shaped edges.
Source : Tsude 1967, 38.

FIG. 35. EARLY IRON SICKLES IN JAPAN

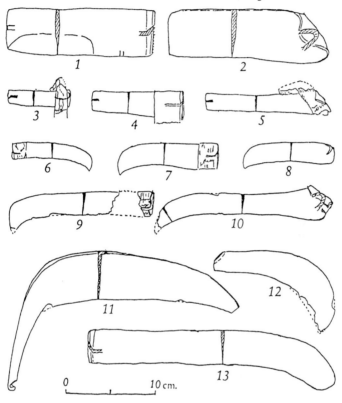

1-5 have straight edges, and 6-13 are developed iron sickles with curved edges.
Source : Tsude 1967, 42.

to reclaim waste land and especially to trample haulms of rice into the paddy-fields[7].

Hiroshi Tsude refers to two periods in the change from wooden farming tools to iron ones : one at the end of the first century, and the other at the middle of the fifth century. In the first period the early iron hoe (Fig. 34 : 1 -5) and the early iron sickle with a straight edge (Fig. 35

FIG. 36. EARLY IRON RAKE-HOES IN JAPAN

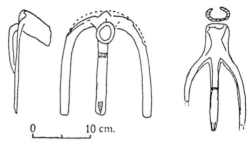

0   10 cm.

Source : Okamoto 1966, 35.

: 1-5) appeared. In the second period the iron hoe or spade with U-shaped edge (Fig. 34 : 6-11) appeared in place of the early iron hoe and was used not only for tilling but also for stirring up the soil of paddy-fields. The iron sickle with a curved edge (Fig. 35 : 6-13) also replaced the one with a straight edge[8], and then the iron rake-hoe appeared (Fig. 36)[9]. From this we know that the change from wooden to iron tools started in the first group and afterwards in the second.

We can find in ancient China and Korea nothing corresponding to these early iron hoes and sickles. They were simply pieces of iron plate turned up at both ends. It is thought that they were made in Japan[10]. But the iron hoe or spade with a U-shaped edge and the iron rake-hoe and the iron sickle with a curved edge seem to have been introduced from South Korea, however, because similar tools were found in the old mounds of South Korea of the fifth or sixth century (Fig. 37 and 38). The iron tool with a U-shaped edge can be used either as a hoe or a spade according to the angle of the shaft, but the fifth or sixth century version seems to have been used as a spade, because the shape of the mouth is very similar to that of the spade, the so-called *Karae*, used in the agriculture of present-day Korea. In the fifth or sixth century, the iron rake-hoes were mostly of one size, but

FIG. 37.   EARLY IRON SPADES AND RAKE-HOES
IN KOREA

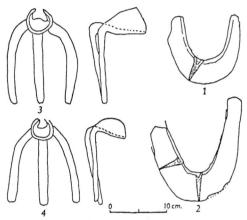

1-2 are iron spade-shoes, and 3-4 are the iron
prongs of rake-hoes.
Source : Arimitsu 1967, 413.

the iron spades came in two sizes : one about 21×16.5cm
and the other about 12×10.5cm.   There are also two
kinds of *Karae* in present-day Korea, the larger being
used with a rope and a team of three men and the smaller kind by one man.   It is thought that the same
methods prevailed in ancient Korea[11].   Kim Chon-hak
insists that the iron age in Korea started in the first
century B. C. at the latest[12], so these iron tools seem to
have been used before the fifth century.   These tools seem
to form part of the large group of tools for various purposes which were manufactured in Korea, which had an
advanced technology, and were introduced from Korea to
Japan after the fifth century[13].

This advanced technology appears to have been introduced from North China to Korea.   Fig. 39 shows the
iron farming tools of the Chan-kuo period of China (403-
221 B. C.)[14].   We can find the original of the Korean and

129

FIG. 38.   EARLY IRON SICKIES WITH CURVED
EDGES IN KOREA

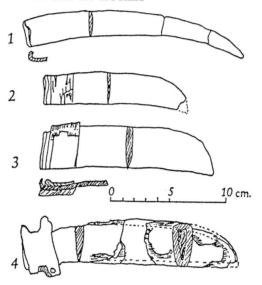

1-2 are iron spade-shoes, and 3-4 are the iron
prongs of rake-hoes.
Source : Arimitsu 1967, 415.

Japanese iron sickle with a curved edge in Fig. 39 : 10,11,
but we cannot find that of the iron rake-hoe and the hoe
or spade with a U-shaped edge in Fig. 39.   The hoe or
spade of China seems to have been developed into the
one with a U-shaped edge in South Korea, because the
climate of South Korea is more humid than that of North
China[15], and the soil of North China is loess (light yellow
soil) whilst that of South Korea is the heavy, muddy soil
of rice fields.   On the other hand, the rake-hoe seems to
have been introduced to South Korea and Japan from the
Yang-tsu-chiang valley in the third century B. C., and
developed into the iron rake-hoe in South Korea.   The
wooden rake-hoe was already found in the first stage of

Japanese agriculture, and was not needed in the loess of North China, whereas it was necessary in the muddy soil of South Korea.

(3) Plough shares in Japan.

Two early examples have been found, one in an ancient mound in the Shimane district of Northwest Japan. The mound seems to have been made in the sixth or seventh century (Fig. 40 :1)[16]. The other share was found in a mound in Miyazaki city in Southwest Japan. This mound seems to have been made in the seventh century (Fig. 40 : 2)[17]. These iron shares are all U-shaped.

Sadasuke Ikata assumed from the archaeological and literary evidence that wheat and barley were introduced from South Korea to Japan in the fifth or sixth century[18] and that oxen were introduced from South Korea at the same time. We cannot find any bones of oxen in ancient mounds in Japan. The first clay figure of an ox was found in an ancient mound of the fifth or sixth century in the Nara district of Middle Japan. On the other hand, in Korea the bones of oxen were found in a shell-mound at Kyong-sang Namdo in South Korea, dating from the first or second century, and in *Sangokushiki* (the first piece of Korean literature) we can find a description of ploughing by oxen at the end of the fifth century or at the beginning of the sixth century[19].

In Korea there is only one presumed example of a plough share (Fig. 41), from an ancient mound at Kyong-sang Nam-do. Its width is about 30cm, and it seems to have been made in the fifth or sixth century. Kyoichi Arimitsu insists that it is a fragment of a share on the analogy of archaeological data like clay figures[20]. It is, therefore, thought that the above-mentioned two examples of ancient Japanese shares were introduced from South Korea in the fifth of sixth century together with wheat,

FIG. 39 IRON FARMING TOOLS OF THE CHAN-KUO PERIOD IN CHINA

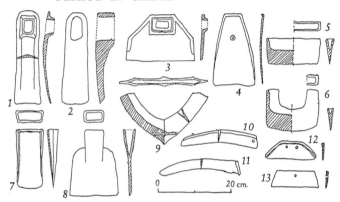

1-3 : hoes ; 4-6 : hoes or spades ; 7-8 : hoes, spades or axes ; 9 : plough share ; 10-13 : sickles.
Source : Sekino 1959, 62-64.

FIG. 40. EARLY PLOUGH SHARE IN JAPAN

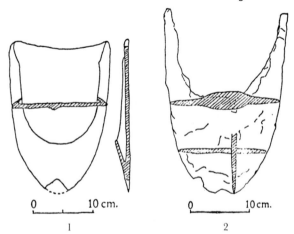

1. A plough share of the 6th or 7th Century in Japan.
2. A plough share of the 7th Century in Japan.
Source : 1. Okamoto 1966, 35 and 2. Suzuki 1966, 35.

FIG. 41. FRAGMENT OF AN
EARLY PLOUGH
SHARE (?) FROM
KOREA

FIG. 42. IRON PLOUGH
SHARE OF THE
END OF THE
CHAN-KUO PE-
RIOD IN CHINA

0   10 CYR

Source : Arimitsu 1967, Plate 845.

Source : Sekino 1959, 29.

FIG. 43. PLOUGHING SCENES FROM FIGURE-STONES
OF THE HAN PERIOD IN CHINA

Source : (right) Liu 1963, 15. (left) Amano 1962, 755 (right).

(below) Amano 1962, 755.

133

FIG. 44-a **PLOUGH OF THE SUNG-PERIOD IN CHINA**   FIG. 44-b **PLOUGH OF THE YÜAN PERIOD IN CHINA**

Source : Amano, 1962, 775.

Source : Wang Vol. 12.

FIG. 45.   **NE-NO-HI-KARA-SUKI DRAWN BY AN OX**

1. an illustration in Kako Genzei Ingakyo
2. correction by S. Tanaka
3. so re-correction by H. Simizu
Source : Simizu 1953, Vol. 1, 365.

barley and oxen.

Ploughing by oxen seems to have started in China in the latter half of the Ch'un-ch'in period (770-413 B. C.), but there is no proof of this[21]. The first iron shares of China were found in a tomb in Hê-nan-shêng at the end of the Chan-kuo period. There were seven, all V-shaped shares, measuring 17.9×12.5cm or 18×23.5cm or 18.5× 17.5cm in size (Fig. 42, cf. Fig. 39)[22]. A Chinese scholar says that these shares were very narrow and had no mould-boards, and that, compared with the modern plough, they were not effective and were not good for tilling deeply[23]. But, as mentioned above, the type of agriculture in North China is "dry-farming", so it probably was not necessary to till deeply and turn the soil over. This type of share is suitable for the "dry-farming" of North China. Later on, in the Han period (206 B.C.- 219 A. D.), the share assumed the shape of an almost regular triangle[24].

If the iron hoe or spade of North China developed into the one with an U-shaped edge in South Korea, the V-shaped iron share of North China may also have developed into the U-shaped share in South Korea, and later on, introduced from South Korea to Japan.

How were these shares used ? They were probably pulled by a rope, as can be seen in Fig. 43 (figure-stones of the Han period)[25]. Later on, wood replaced the rope, and the Chinese plough came into being as the long-sole plough. Fig. 44-a shows the plough of the Sung period (960-1279)[26], and Fig. 44-b that of the Yüan period (1271 -1368)[27]. The Japanese plough which had been from ancient times till the nineteenth century was of the same type.

It is not certain whether the Ne-no-hi-kara-suki of Shôsôin is a plough or a spade. If it is a spade, its wooden shaft is too curved. Fig. 45 : 1 shows an illustration of *Kako-genzai-inga-kyô*. Its original seems to have been drawn at the beginning of the eighth century in

China judging from the costume of the farmer, and was later introduced to Japan. Fig. 45 : 1 shows what seems to be a copy made in the Nara period[28]. As Sakujiro Tanaka insisted, as a plough it seems to have been pulled by an ox as shown in Fig. 45 : 2, but Fig. 45 : 3 is a corrected version of Fig. 45 : 2 by Hiroshi Simizu[29].

If Ne-no-hi-kara-suki was used in the manner shown in Fig. 45 : 3, it must have been difficult to till the soil effectively, because its share was too narrow. The width is 18.5×12cm, whereas the width of those found in the Shimane district is 25×18cm and that of the one found in Miyazaki city is 20×21cm. Therefore, Ne-no-hi-kara-suki seems to have been made in the eighth century in Japan only for the ceremony, imitating the ploughs introduced from South Korea.

Notes

(1) Shôsôin Interpretation Plate 1.

(2) Fig. 32 is Plate 1 and Plate 2 in Shôsôin.

(3) Fig. 32 is Plate 3 in Shôsôin.

(4) Shôsôin,interpretation of Plates 1-3

(5) The author thinks Dr. Andô's theory is the most reasonable. Andô pp. 5-59. However Dr. Andô thinks that the date of introduction of rise cultivation into Japan is the 2nd century B. C. ; but it must be corrected to the 3rd century B. C. according to Kôkogakkai pp. 30-32.

(6) Kinoshita pp. 233-249. Fig. 33 is Plate 1 in Kinoshita p. 235.

(7) Okamoto p. 35.

(8) Tsude pp. 36-51. Fig. 34 is Plate 1 in Tsude p. 38, and Fig. 35 is Plate 3 in ibid. p. 42.

(9) Okamoto pp. 34-35. Fig. 36 is Plate 5 in Okamoto p. 35.

(10) Tsude pp. 43-44.

(11) Arimitsu pp. 414-416. Fig. 37 is Plate 1 in Arimitsu p. 413, and Fig. 38 is Plate 2 in ibid. p. 415

(12) Ishida p. 175.

(13) Tsude p. 50 ; Ueda pp. 69-96.

(14) Sekino pp. 62-64. Fig. 39 is Plate 23 in Sekino .63.

(15) For example, the annual rainfall of Pei-ping (North China) is 599 mm, on the other hand, that of Taegu (South Korea)

979 mm, and that of Chunji (South Korea) 1241 mm. in Hatakeyama.

(16) Okamoto p. 34 ; Tanaka p. 127 ; Fig. 40 : 1 is Plate 5 in Okamoto p. 35.

(17) Suzuki pp. 23-25. Fig. 40 : 2 is a Plate in Suzuki p. 24.

(18) Ikata 1941 pp. 78-101.

(19) Ikata 1945 pp. 278-450.

(20) Arimitsu p. 416 ; Fig. 41 is Plate 845 in Chôsen sôtokufu.

(21) Takeshi Sekino and Motonosuke Amano consider that ploughing by oxen is required for iron shares ; in China iron tools appeared in the middle of the Ch'un-ch'in period, so ploughing by oxen seems to have started in the latter half of this period. Sekino pp. 27-29 ; Amano pp. 737-756 ; Fig. 42 is Plate 12 in Sekino. 29.

(22) Report 82, 91.

(23) Report p. 82.

(24) Amano p. 751.

(25) Fig. 43, right 1 is Plate in Liu p. 15 ; Fig. 43 left and 43 below are Plates in Amano p. 775.

(26) Fig. 44 a is a Plate in Amano p. 775.

(27) Fig. 44 b is Plates in Wang.

(28) Amano p. 771.

(29) Simizu 1953, Vol. 1, 365.

THREE

The Development of Ploughs in Japan

In 1969 I described an early Japanese plough Ne-no-hi-kara-suki of Shôsôin, in : *Tools and Tillage* Vol. 1 No. 2 (see the former chapter). This chapter expands that study with recent materials and studies, and describes the development of ploughs in Japan from early times to the middle of the 20th century.

As I described in Part I chapter 2, there are two basic types of ploughs used in the world. One, used in the dry zone, is suitable for shallow tillage to conserve the water in the soil. The other, used in the humid zone, is suitable for deep tillage for weeding. Deep tillage in the dry zone is bad for soil water conservation, while shallow tillage in the humid zone is not effective for weeding. According to the theory of the "index of aridity" invented by a French meteorologist E. de Mertonne (Maronne 24, 250), the northern part of China is in the dry zone, and South China, Korea and Japan are quite clearly in the humid zone. It hardly needs to be stated, therefore, that the plough wich probably came into being during the Ch'unch'in period (770-413 B. C.) in North China, was of the shallow ploughing type (Sekino 27 - 29 ; Amano 1962, 736 and Amano 1956, 82, 91). Fig. 42 shows one of seven iron plough shares unearthed from the Chan-kuo period (403-211 B. C.) grave in Huixian (Henan). Three were quite fragmentary and the remaining four were V-shaped plough-shares, but only two of these were perfect

FIG. 46. WOODEN TOY UNEARTHED AT WUWEI
(GANSU) OF THE HAN PERIOD IN CHINA

Source : Yomiuri 1979, 58.

V-shaped shares. The lengths of these four shares were
17.9cm, 17.5cm, 18cm and 18.5cm. The width of the last
two (perfect) shares was 23.5cm (Chûgoku ... 82, 91).

According to Guo Bao-gou : "This plough is small and
narrow and not suitable for deep tillage" (Chûgoku 82)
and Huang Zhan-yue says : "Observation of the excavated
plough-shares shows that the neck has an angle of 120°,
but each wing only measures 10cm. Even if these
ploughs were pulled by oxen they could not till very
deeply" (Huang 105, cited in Amano 1962, 737).

Until recently, scenes from figure-stones were the only
available sources for ascertaining the use of the plough
and the way in which the share was attached to the body
of the plough (Fig. 43) (Amano 1962, 755). Recently,
however, the Han period (206 B. C. —220 A. D.) wooden
toy unearthed at Wuwei (Gansu) has offered fresh in-
formation (Fig. 46) (Yomiruri Fig. 58). This shows that
the plough-share was attached to the wooden sole of the
plough parallel to the surface of the ground. With this
type of plough the soil cannot be tilled deeply and

139

turned, but only shallowly mixed. It is suitable for the dry zone only. This plough of the Han period closely resembles the plough which was until recently used in Okinawa (the most southern part of Japan), in the Yaeyama archipelago (Fig. 47). According to an old man spoken to me at Hateruma island in the Yaeyama archipelago, the plough-share was bought from a blacksmith and the rest of the plough was made in wood by the farmer himself to his own size. This type of plough with a long sole is now generally classified as a "long-sole plough". From the Han period until the present time, all Chinese ploughs have been of this long-sole type (Amano 1962, 836).

In my earlier study I wrote : "Two early examples have been found, one in an ancient mound in the Shimane district of Northwest Japan. The mound seems to have been made in the sixth or seventh century. The other share was found in a mound in Miyazaki city in Southwest Japan. This mound seems to have been made in the seventh century." (Fig. 40) (Iinuma 1969, 11 Fig. 11, 12). But, according to Tadashi Kinoshita's recent research, the first plough share cannot be traced back earlier than the Muromahi perido (1392-1568) (Kinoshita 648), and the second blabe was probably not for a plough but a large spade[1]. As these two exmples are a little doubtful, the oldest known example of a plough in Japan are two : the first is excavated recently in Sakaide of the South Japan. It is a kind of a long sole plough and seems to have been made in the 7th Century (Fig. 48). The second example is the Ne-no-hi-kara-suki of Shôsôin, as earlier described (Iinuma 1969, 106).

As we have seen, in China from the Han period onwards, all ploughs were of the long-sole type. In East Asia the earliest examples of shares came from North China, then they seem to have been introduced from North China to Japan via Korea. However, what I would like to make clear now is that the Ne-no-hi-kara-

140

suki is a plough without a sole. If that is so the question remains of how the northern Chinese Han period long-sole plough changed into the no-sole plough, such as the Ne-no-hi-kara-suki.

I wrote earlier : "In Korea there is only one presumed example of a plough-share from an ancient mound at Kyong-sang-Nam-do" (Iinuma 1969, 112, Fig. 13). But four certain plough-shares were found recently in Korea. They were excavated from two ancient mounds of the Three Kingdoms period (356-668 A. D.) (Azuma 536-538). One found at Yong-sung-ri, An-byun-gun (Ham-kyung Nam-do) has a total length of 21cm, and a share width (at the widest point) of 10cm and a long thin blade point (Fig. 49. 2). It is necessary to find proof of its use as either an ox-drawn or a hand-held tool, but I think it can be taken to be ox-drawn. From the fact that the share width is narrow compared with the total length of the share, it was probably used for making the ridge in the fields and for cultivating between crops.

The second site, Kuson-dong in the south area of Han river, yielded three plough-shares. One has a length of 44.4cm, a share width of 34.4cm and on the back is a V-shaped opening (Fig. 49. 1). The second has a length of abut 25cm, a share width of 26cm and a V-shaped opening. At the base of the body of the share there is what appears to be a rectangular opening, probably for attaching the plough shaft. The third has a length of about 21cm, a share width of about 24cm and one part a triangular dent in the body and two small openings. The three shares are all slightly different in shape and size and one can of course infer a difference in use. Nevertheless I think they belong to ploughs without a sole. The fact that in the field farming area of Yong-sung-ri and the paddy-field farming area of Kuson-dong, different shaped plough-shares should be unearthed, is indeed very interesting. The Kuson-dong ancient mound dated at the latest to sixth century and the Yong-sung-ri mound to the

FIG. 47.   PLOUGH OF ISHIGAKI ISLAND, OKINAWA IN JAPAN

Source : the author

FIG. 48.   PLOUGH-SHARE UNEARTHED AT SAKAIDA OF THE SOUTH JAPAN

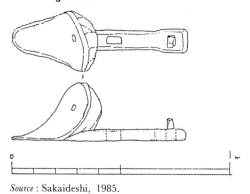

Source : Sakaideshi, 1985.

142

late sixth or early seventh century, which shows that ox-drawn ploughing almost certainly existed in the sixth century. According to the archaeological materials and old records, *Benshin-den* in *Gishi* (the old Chinese historical book) and *Shiragi-honki* in *Sangoku-shiki* (the old Korean historical book) ox-drawn ploughing in Korea seems to be dated back one or two centuries from the sixth century.

Also in Korea in the Three Kingdoms period not so much plough-shares as the *tôguwa* (a kind of hoe), three-pronged hoes and U-shaped spades have been unearthed (Fig. 50) (see Iinuma 1969 Fig. 53). Of these, the most important for paddy-field cultivation are the U-shaped spades. Of those found there are two general varieties : large and small, the large blade having a width of 18.4cm and length of 17.2cm and the small blade a width of 10.5cm and a length of 12cm (Fig. 49. 3-7) (Nôrinshô ... 101 ; Azuma 533-534). In Japan from the third century B. C. the hoe was a very important implement, especially in the Edo period (1603-1867) when it was widespread all over the country, adapted to the particular area and soil type. In Korea, on the other hand, the hoe did not develop into various types and was less widely used than in Japan (Shimizu 1979, 689-691 ; Nôrinshô ... 98). Instead of the Japanese hoe, the plough and the spade were more important. In Japan the spade was used more as a general than as an agricultural tool.

Nowadays in Korea there are two types of spade. One is the *karae* which has two holes in the spade head to which are attached two thick ropes (Fig. 51). The spade is used with two to six people pulling the ropes and one person holding the long handle behind. It is most frequently used by three people. The *tabi* on the other hand is much smaller and used by one person (Fig. 52). Almost certainly the large Korean U-shaped spade was used jointly while the small one was used by an individual in ealier times in Korea.

The long-sole of the long-sole plough disturbs deep

143

FIG. 49. PLOUGH SHARES AND SPADE SHOES IN THE THREE KINGDOMS PERIOD IN KOREA

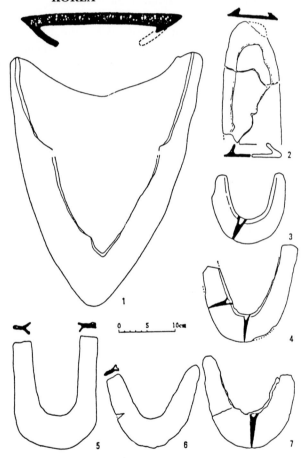

(1) Kusung-dong   (2) Young-sung-ri   (3) Kyong-gju   (4) Kyo-gju
(5) Kusun-dong   (6) Inwang-dong   (7) Hwang-nam-ri.
Source : Azuma 1979, 533-534.

FIG. 50. LOCATION OF THE OID MOUNDS WHERE
AGRICULTURAL IMPLEMENTS HAVE BEEN
FOUND IN KOREA

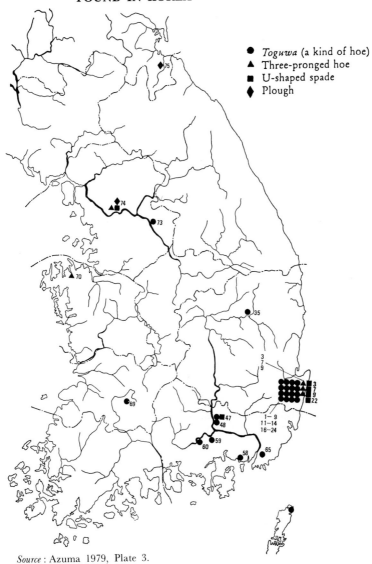

● *Toguwa* (a kind of hoe)
▲ Three-pronged hoe
■ U-shaped spade
◆ Plough

Source : Azuma 1979, Plate 3.

145

ploughing and at the same time balances the plough. It was ideally suitable to the dry zone like in North China. On the other hand, the no-sole plough without the help of the sole can of course cultivate to any depth, but it is very unstable. This type is suitable for a humid zone such as South Korea. This is surely the basic reason that the long-sole plough of North China changed to the no-sole plough in Korea, but in the Three Kingdoms period, compared with the Han period in North China, there were very few plough-drawing oxen, so it is probable that in this period in Korea the long-sole plough which had originated in North China was drawn by people rather than oxen. And this was most probably also true of the spade with the U-shaped iron shoe (especially the large U-shaped spade).

At a later period, the spread of the plough in Korea was quite marked and much more widespread than in Japan. In the fifteenth century Korean agricultural book *Nojichokusetsu* there are references to crop cultivation which could be thought to refer to the use of the plough. In field cultivation, the process of ploughing, sowing the seeds, covering them, pressing and later weeding etc. was, even in the poor household, all carried out by the use of oxen rather than of human beings. In Reports of Agricultural Surveys in Korea from 1905 there is the following description : "The skilled and widespread use of the plough in Korea can not be compared with Japan" (Nôshômushô 1905, 435). "The tools themselves may not be perfect, but they are used better than in Japan. There are many types of plough : *mottate-zuki, sokozuki* and they were made in many ways" (Nôshômushô 1905, 371). This description shows that at the beginning of the twentieth century ploughing had developed more in Korea than in Japan.

The *mottate-zuki* in Japanese means the no-sole plough, and the *soko-zuki* the long-sole plough. We know, therefore, that there were both the no-sole plough and the

146

FIG. 51. KARAE (A KIND OF SPADE)

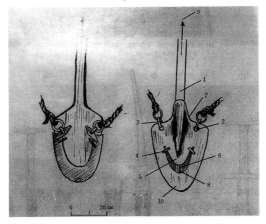

Source : Government of the Republic of Korea 1969 ;
Fig. 37.

FIG. 52. TABI(A KIND OF SPADE)

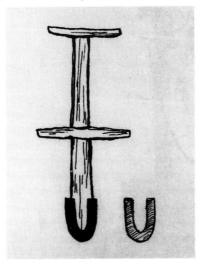

Source : Government of the Republic of
Korea 1969 ; Fig. 35.

147

long-sole plough in Korea in 1905. At that time the traditional ploughs there were, one-ox ploughs, two-ox ploughs, the long-sole plough and the no-sole plough. The no-sole plough, the *Yeonjang* in Korean (Fig. 53) was used in the fields and the long-sole plough, the *Janggi* in Korean (Fig. 54) in paddy fields. In North Korea the large plough drawn by two oxen was used, because there were many fields and also because of the planting rotation system. Further south the plough was smaller and was drawn by one ox. Perhaps, from the Three Kingdoms period to the twentieth century, there had been both the no-sole plough for fields and the long-sole plough for paddy fields in Korea, and as there were more fields than paddy fields in earlier Korea so the use of the no-sole plough was probably more widespread than the use of the long-sole plough. At that time, both the no-sole plough and the long-sole plough seem to have been introduced from Korea to Japan.

As described in my study referred to above, at the beginning of the year, the ceremony in which the emperor used the plough came from China. Almost certainly the practice came to Japan through Korea. And at the same time it is likely that the Ne-no-hi-kara-suki, that is the no-sole plough, came to Japan from Korea. On the other hand, in Japan, in the *Engishiki* (the Collection of Laws and Regulations) of 927, there are records of tools used on the imperial farm, which may refer to the long-sole plough. In the dictionary *Wamyoruijusho* produced around the same time (931–938), *kara-suki* was described as the long-sole plough. After that, all ploughs represented pictorially in Japan were of the long-sole type. For example, a plough drawn in *Matsugasaki-tenzin-engi-emaki* (1311), one of the pictures of the *emaki* type (the pictures-scroll) which was popular in the eleventh-fourteenth centuries, was the long-sole plough. All ploughs in the illustrations of agricultural books, which were written in the Edo period, were of the long-sole type. We know therefore,

148

FIG. 53. YEONJANG (THE NO-SOLE PLOUGH)

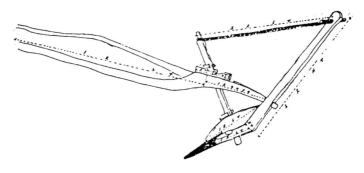

Source : Chosen Sōtokufu 1924, Fig. 29.

FIG. 54. JANGGI (THE LONG-SOLE PIOUGH)

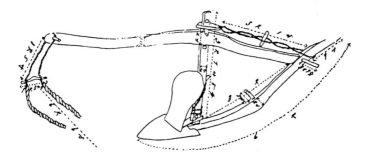

Source : Chosen Sōtohufu 1924, Fig. 1.

that Japanese ploughs were generally of the long-sole type after *Engishiki*.

Why did the dry zone cultivation type long-sole plough become so widespread in the humid zone type cultivation of Japan ? Of course from early times till the twentieth century there was a very strong influence from Chinese and Korean cultures, but on top of that there are, I think, two possible technical reasons. The first is that

149

Fig. 55. THE COURSE OF THE DEVELOPMENT OF JPANESE PLOUGHS

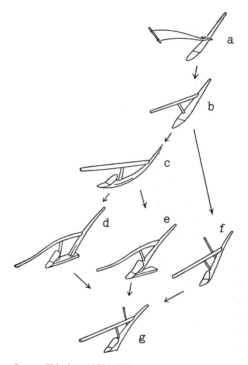

Source : Shimizu 1979, 690.

the purpose of deep ploughing is to fertilize the soil and increase its production. If it is not possible to enrich the soil with much fertilizer, then deep ploughing leads to poor production and shallow ploughing is better. The second reason is that to make the unpermeated base in the paddy fields, the long-sole of the long-sole plough is particularly suitable. Even in the *Edo* period, when commercial fertilizers were produced and the hoe and spade were used for deep tillage, nevertheless the long-sole plough continued to be used in the paddy fields.

Hiroshi Shimizu asserts that the long-sole plough de-

FIG. 56. **THE TRADITIONAL LONG-SOLE PLOUGH IN
JAPAN**

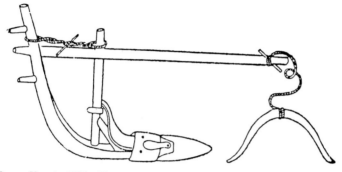

Source : Yasuda 1952, 45.

veloped out of the no-sole plough in Japan. He traces
the course of the Japanese plough from a-shape to d-
shape (Fig. 55). The evidence for this development in,
for example, the Kinki region (the middle part of Japan),
was earlier found in the Ne-no-hi-kara-suki type which is
typical of the a-shape, and ploughs used in the second
half of the nineteenth century in the same area which
were of the d- and e-shapes. As the Chinese and South-
East Asian ploughs turn to the right and the Japanese
plough turns to the left, so it is probably misleading to
suppose that a fixed shape of plough was introuced into
ancient Japan. It is possible that Japan had developed
her own plough from the primitive no-sole plough which
probably still did not have a fixed shape by the Kamakura period (the twelfth-fourteenth century). From the
fact that in the second half of the nineteenth cetury there
were very varied shapes of plough distributed all over
Japan, one can infer that the no-sole plough had not been
completely standardized in early times as Hiroshi Shimizu
suggests (Shimizu 1979, 689-691).

But from the surviving records and artifacts it is hard
to accept Shimizu's suggestion that in pre-*Engishiki* Japan

151

(early ninth century) so many types of the no-sole plough had spead all over the country. It is possible that at that time the hoe was the main culitivating tool and the plough was restricted to farming connected with the imperial farms. Also, although present day (before about 1960) ploughs are mostly right-turning, historically this was not necessarily so (after abut 1960, the ploughs were completely replaced by the machines). In the second half of the nineteenth century left-turning ploughs were in use along the Japan-Sea coast, while the Kanto area (the east part of Japan) used right turning ploughs and the Kochi prefecture (the south-west part of Japan) had right turning ploughs (Kishida 23-25). Therefore, I think that the long-sole plough did not derive from the no-sole plough in Japan as Shimizu asserts, but that both the no-sole plough and long-sole plough were introduced from Korea into early Japan as I described above, the former being used in the fields, and the latter in the paddy fields as in Korea. But in almost all parts of Japan the hoe has been used in the fields, and in many parts of Japan the hoe had to be used even in the paddy fields.

Shimizu also says that "the use of the no-sole plough was not completely excluded. Although most ploughs were long-sole type, in the prefectures of Gumma, Chiba, Kanagawa, Gifu, Tottori, Shimane, Fukuoka and Nagasaki, the no-sole plough was being used in the second half of the nineteenth century. But these prefectures were the under-developed areas for agriculture at that time" (Shimizu 1979, 691-723). Among these prefectures, however, Fukuoka and Nagasaki were the most developed areas of agriculture at that time. These prefectures had maintained close connection with Korea from early times. According to Masao Tsukikawa in the Nagasaki prefecture the no-sole plough was used until recently in the fields [2]. In *Nagasakiken Noguzu*, 1880 (Illustrations of Agricultural Implements in Nagasaki prefecture) several no-sole ploughs were recorded. In Tsuhima island in the

FIG. 57. THE TRADITIONAL NO-SOLE PLOUGH IN JAPAN

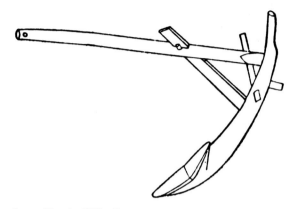

Source : Yasuda 1952, 45.

Nagasaki prefecture the no-sole plough was used for field cultivation already in the 17th century (*Rono Ruigo,* 1722), and there was a domain of Tsushima island in the Fukuoka Prefecture before in the 19th century. It is specially significant that this island is the nearest point to Korea in Japan (the distance from Tsushima to Korea is about 40 km) and has had trade links with Korea in the Edo period (even though Japan was otherwise completely closed to all foreign countries at that period), and as the no-sole plough was used for field cultivation in Korea, it is likely that the field cultivation by the no-sole plough spread to the Nagasaki and Fukuoka prefectures via the trade links between Tsuhima and Korea. It is thought that the no-sole plough was first adapted to the paddy fields from the fields in Fukuoka prefecture in the second half of the nineteenth century. It is not known, of course, whether this change was made by an individual or by a group of farmers. It is hardly necessary to mention, however, that at that time the increase in demand for rice and the increase in use of fertilizers probably promoted this change. It was the first case of deep tillage in the paddy fields by the plough in Japan (Fig. 56, 57).

There was an episode in 1881 which showed the general condition of paddy field cultivation, when the government assembled excellent farmers in Tokyo for the All Japan Agricultural Conference, Zenkoku-nodankai. Here, Chuzaburo Koda, a farmer in Nara prefecture (the middle part of Japan), said "I compared the use of men or oxen for cultivation ; men can certainly cultivate deeper" (Nômushô 1881, 727). That is, it was not possible to cultivate deeply using an ox-drawn plough (the long-sole plough). For deep tillage, tools used by hand (the hoe or spade) were more effective. But, in Europe and America deep tillage was done by the plough at that time, therefore it would not be surprising if Westen agricultural scholars who were in national agricultural schools then at the invitation of the Japanese govermment were confused by this condition. For example, Max Fesca, a German teacher at the Komaba national agricultural school, pointed out clearly the adverse effects of the traditional Japanese method of shallow tillage. He travelled throughout Japan and carried out agronomic surveys at many places. He lived in Japan for 12 years (1882-1894), during which time he published many articles and books about Japanese agriculture. All his books were received quite favourably at the time (Saegusa et al. p. 249). In Nogyo Kairyo An (A Plan for Improving Japanese Agriculture), for example, he wrote in 1881 :

"The main defects of Japanese agriculture as I have seen are as follows :
1. The tillage is not deep enough.
2. The drainage is not complete.
3. The fertilizer itself is expensive, and its quantity is not large enough ; at the same time, the methods of application are not correct.
4. The system of crop rotation is not correct.

FIG. 58. THE MODERN SHORT SOLE PLOUGH IN JAPAN

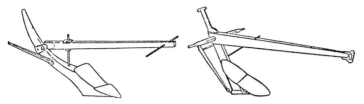

1. Marukozuki
Source : Yasuda 1952, 50.

2. Matsuyamazuki
Source : Yasuda 1952, 51.

3. Takakitazuki (The complet form of the modern short sole plough)
Source : the author

If we cultivate the soil deeply, the surface soil grows in volume. Therefore the roots of plants can without difficuly grow deep into the soil and can take nourishment from the applied fertilizer as well as from the natural compost found there. Thus, even if the plants sometimes suffer from want of rain, we can minimize the damage.

In Japan, however, it often happens that, in spite of the large quantity of fertilizer applied the harvest of crops is very poor. This may be because the nutrition of the

fertilizer, along with rain water, penetrates the soft surface soil into the solid soil, and since the solid soil is too
hard for the roots to penetrate, they cannot take up any
nutrition that is contained in the solid soil. Deep tillage
is harmful only when the thin seam of the fertile and
rather heavy soil covers a poor soil or a very light soil
through which rain water permeates very easily. Except
for this type of soil, deep tillage is very effetive for obtaining a rich harvest. In Japan, the depth of tillage is, in
the main, only between 9 to 15cm. It is essential that we
should cultivate the soil to at least 18cm and sometimes
as deep as 30cm, as the case may be. The best plough
for deep tillage that I have seen in this country is the no-
sole plough of Fukuoka prefecture (the depth of tillage is
more than 30cm; its price is 85 sen). Deep tillage is
most effective only in the dry field, for when water
gathers in the undersoil, it is usually harmful for the
roots of the plants. Therefore in wet fields it is necessary
to complete the drainage" (Fesca 1939, p. 1756).

We can see that the essentials of the new method of
rice cultivation, which depend on deep tillage using the
no-sole plough, are clearly advocated. Fesca recom-
mended the no-sole plough of Fukuoka prefecture and
gave an illustration of it in his chief work *Nihon Chisan
Ron* (A Study on Japanese Agriculture) (Fesca 1891, 349).

Deep tillage in the paddy fields by the no-sole plough
spread rapidly along with the new method of rice cultivation all over Japan. But for the no-sole plough, its merit
was at the same time its demerit; that is, it had no sole.
This made it possible to cultivate deeper, but also demanded much more physical srength and mechanical
skill, because the no-sole plough was very unstable.
Therefore the diffusion of the no-sole plough led immediately to a unanimous demand for a plough suitable
for deep tillage which did not require so much physical
strength and mechanical skill. Two solutions were considered at the time : one was to make the western plough

smaller and more suitable for Japanese small-scale farming (the average farm size was about oue hectare) ; the
other was to invent a new plough for the purpose. The
former solution was promoted actively mainly by the
graduates of the Komaba national agricultural school,
while the latter was promoted exclusively by private
citizens (particularly by dealers in farming tools familiar
with farmers in the county districts). The plough invented by those private citizens was the short-sole plough.
Even as early as the Edo period, a short-sole plought had
been used in a certain district in the south-west part of
Japan (for example, Nagasaki and Fukuoka prefectures).
This short-sole plough, however, had many defects and
was not widely adopted. Among the several varieties of
the short-sole plough, the one which had developed in
Kumamoto prefecture (in the south-west part of Japan)
seemed to be superior and on the basis of it Suejiro Otsu,
an agricultural implement trader in a village in the northern part of Kumamoto prefecture, invented the *Maruko-
zuki*, the first instance of the modern short-sole plough
(Fig. 58. 1)

It was in March 1899 that he applied for a patent, so
the invention was probably made in the previous year.
He had set up a special research room in his house and
had studied hard night and day. *Maruko-zuki* was given a
favourable reception as a solution to the demands of the
time, but it required a naturally curved piece of wood as
the plough body, so it was impossible to mass produce.
Furthermore, it was designed for a fixed plough-share.
Later this sort of plough was improved and produced in
quantity at both Isono and Fukami factories in Fukuoka
(Shimizu 746-751).

Quite apart from these movements in the south-west
part of Japan, Genzo Matsuyama of Nagano prefecture
(the middle part of Japan), in about 1900, invented a
new short-sole plough (Fig. 58. 2). This was different
from *Maruko-zuki* with its fixed plough-share made of cast-

157

iron in that it had a movable plough-share made of steel. It represented a substantial advance in the development of the short-sole plough. Matuyama had attended elemetary school for 4 years, and had then become an assistant to a teacher of the no-sole plough; following that he had overcome great difficulties in inventing his plough. He himself made a steel plough-share from a traditional steel saw (Kisida).

The most important plough invention after *Matsuyama-suki* was *Takakita-zuki*, Shinjiro Takakita in Mie prefecture (the middle part of Japan) invented a short-sole plough which was much more suitable for deeper cultivation that the *Matsuyama* plough (achieving more than twice the depth of tillage), and it had ingenious contrivances. For example, it had two movable plough-shares and two movable slatted mouldboards. We may say that the modern short-sole plough was perfected by Takakita (Fig. 58. 3).

Takakita,like Otsu and Matsuyama was not a graduate of national or local highschools or colleges. After his father's bankruptcy, he had been apprenticed to a hardware shop in the country at the age of 12, and had endeavoured to improve various farming tools, especially the plough (Nuokawa and Sakane).

Later these short-sole ploughs diffused rapidly. They quickly supplanted the no-sole plough and became a key feature of the new method of rice cultvation. It can be said that without them, there could not have been much advancement in the new methods of rice cultivation, yet, till now, almost no Japanese scholar has paid due attention to the short-sole plough. On the contrary, agronomists from Komaba national agricultural school (after 1890, Department of Agriculture of Tokyo University) intent on minimizing the Western plough, have assumed a critical attitude toward such short-sole ploughs invented by private citizens. For example in 1904, eminent agronomists (all graduates of Komaba national agricultural school) in a prize contest for improving the plough, rejected all the

26 plans submitted after inspection (Dainihon nôkaihô No. 269, 1904). In the second contest held in the following year, they judged that among the 13 submitted there were no plans worthy of the first and second prizes. They conferred the third prize on Shogoro Saito, Genzo Matsuyama and Suejiro Otsu. Saito's plough which was first among the three was only an imitation of the Western plough (Dainihon nôkaihô No. 306, 1906 and No. 307, 1907).

It is characteristic of the Western plough that the flat plough-share and the side-board constitute a rather stabilizing triangular space, and therefore the stability of the plough is very good. But in deep tillage, when the width of the soil cultivation is too narrow, the soil which is turned over in ploughing turns back again; thus the plough body cannot be made too small. This was the main reason why the small-sized western plough had not been used in Japanese small scale farming.

The modern short-sole plough that was invented and improved by private individuals had quite different qualities from the western plough. It was a highly complicated and delicate plough; it could readily adjust the depth and width of cultivation to the nature of the soil by a simple operation; and it could maintain the same direction of cultivation of soil with the movable plough share when going forward or backward. The Takakita plough in particular is most remarkable; the two plough-shares move quite freely, vertically and horizontally, and from right to left, or vice versa. It is small and elaborate and best suited for deep tillage. This invention is worthy of our prize.

But since about 1960, Japanese industries have been developed rapidly and the demand for industrial labourers has increased rapidly. The Japanese Government has promoted the policy that farmers should save their labour by using agricultural machines and let labourers go to the urban districts to serve industry. As a result, the excellent ploughs for deep tillage were changed to the small farm-tractors for shallow tillage (the depth is 3-5cm), and today we can no longer see these ploughs in the fields and paddy fields.

Notes

(1) A letter from Kinoshita to the author.
(2) Personal communication with Masao Tsukikawa.

FOUR

The Introduction of American and European Agricultural Science into Japan in the Meiji Era

The Meiji era (1868-1912), especially the first half of it, represents both a gap and a period of continuity in the history of Japanese agriculture, as can be illustrated by the example of the plough.

As described above, the Japanese plough, which was used from ancient times to the Meiji era, appears to have been introduced to Japan from North China through Korea in the 7th century. Its chief characteristic is a long sole, after which it is called the long-sole plough. The long sole is suitable for shallow tillage.

In the Meiji era, when Japan started to study European and American agricultural science, the government established agricultural schools and experimental stations and employed European and American agricultural scholars. Some of them, Max Fesca especially, pointed out clearly for the first time the mistake of using the shallow-tillage plough in humid Japan. Fesca recommened the wider use of a no-sole plough which was employed at that time in a part of Japan(Fukuoka Prefecture).

The no-sole plough was the most primitive type of deep-tillage plough with the sole removed altogether, because it gets in the way of deep tillage. The depth of tillage using a no-sole plough was quite irregular and it took great skill to regulate it. As a consequence a short-sole plough was invented at the beginning of the 20th century. It was a kind of deep-tillage plough, but did

not require the same operating skill as the no-sole plough
and it rapidly became widespread throughout Japan at
the latter's expense.

(1) Before the Meiji Restoration

First, the role of the Meiji Restoration in Japanese
history must be clarified. From the 16th to the 19th
centuries Japanese society existed under a system of centralized feudalism similar to that of Tudor England or the
"ancien régime" of France. Th Tokugawa Shoguns were
actually feudal landlords in status, but their power was so
extensive that they could increase, decrease, move or fully
deprive any fief holder in Japan. In particular, to control
the economic development of subordinate feudal landlords
(Daimyos), the Shoguns prohibited all foreign travel by
Japanese nationals, and limited foreign trade to be a
Shogunate-controlled monopoly with only Holland and
China, which was carried on at Nagasaki (but Tsushima
island was only permited to trade to Korea by Shogunate). Consequently the development of the Japanese economy was severely distorted. But the Shoguns and
Daimyos compelled their vassals to live in castle-towns,
thereby separating them from the rural power base of
agriculture and the appended farm population of potential
warriors. In addition the Shoguns compelled the
Daimyos and their vassals to alternate their residence,
living in the Shogunate capital of Edo (now Tokyo) for
one year and then in their own castle-town for another
one year. Consequently this system accelerated the development of commercial and industrial sectors. This
was primarily due to the fact that though the tax allotment of the Shoguns and Daimyos was in rice, and the
Shoguns and Daimyos and their vassals resorted to the
expedient of converting the annual rice tribute into cash
and making cash payments to cover expenses in the
castle-towns. Year by year the population of the castle-

162

towns increated. In 1721, the population of the Chonins
(merchants and craftmen) in Edo was 501.394 according
to the first census close to accuracy. For the sum total of
all castle-town population, about half were the Chonins,
while the half were the Samurais (warriors, their families
and servants). Therefore, the population of Edo in 1721
was certainly more than 1,000.000. At that time, no
other city in the world had a population greater than
1,000.000. Even the largest city of Europe and America,
London had a population of only 500.000 at the beginning of th 18th century, whille at the beginning of the
19th century the population of London stood at around
900.000. On the other hand, the population of the other
castle-towns of the Daimyos were smaller, and at the
beginning of the 18th century ranged between 10.000 and
100.000. At that time Kyoto, residence of the Emperor
and his family, and Osaka, the largest commercial city,
had each population of about 350.000. Such growth of
the cities was supported by the rapid growth of agricultural production. As the Shoguns and Daimyos graunted
the holding rights over farmland to the farmers, the farmers endeavored to convert desolate land into farmland,
and to improve agricultural technology. For instance the
farmers invented special hoes for deep-tillage and new
threshing machines, and converted from primary dependence on green manure to the use of nightsoil for crop
fertilization. Additionally, the wealthy class of farmers
began to use "money-manure", that is oilseed cake and
dried herring and sardines. By such development in agriculture, the land owning class became established
amongst farmers, and gardened a par of the annual rice
tribute by farmers, to the feudal lords.

The development of a flourishing town-life promoted
the expansion of commerce and industry. In contrast to
the revolutionary power of the bourgeoisie an landowner
classes in France and England, in Japan though these
classees had become well established economically, they

163

had not been able to overthrow the feudal political state by the middle of the 19th century. In 1853-4 the United States Navy commanded by Admiral Perry, forced entry into the Bay of Edo, and compelled the Shogunate to enter into diplomatic relations with capitalist powers. Consequantly, extreme economic and political confusion reigned at this time in Japan, and a faction of lower echelon of the Samurai class proceeded to destroy the feudal power of the Shogunate. That was the Meiji Restoration, which essentially amounted to a bourgeois revolution.

(2) Industrialization

The Meiji government endeavored to develop agriculture and industry to reach the economic level of the industrial capitalist powers as soon as possible. It established many factories following European and American models, and transferred them to private control from 1881. Consequently from 1887 to the first world war, Japan went through its industrial revolution. The most impotant industry contributing to this development was the cotton industry. In the Edo period the cotton industry had already begun to flourish in the neighbouring areas of the large cities. By the entrance into diplomatic relations with the capitalist powers, cheep strong high-quality cotton thread was imported in bulk. As a result, the weaving sector of the cotton industry converted to the use of the imported, thread, thereby displacing the thread produced the Japanese spinning sector of it from the market and effectively destroying that sector. After the Meiji Restoration, spinning factories were established on the same technical principle as English model in order to supply the weaving sector of the cotton industry. From 1890, it was possible to export the new cotton thread to Korea and China (Table 12).

As described above, the landowner class was estab-

TABLE 12 PRODUCTION, IMPORT, EXPORT, AND CONSUMPTION OF COTTON YARN IN JAPAN, 1889-1900

(unit *kori*=180kg)

	Production	Import	Export	Consumption
1889	67,046	142,703	31	209,749
90	104,839	106,361	108	211,169
91	144,980	57,792	109	202,664
92	204,950	81,028	1,053	285,869
93	214,758	64,684	11,796	278,389
94	294,400	53,143	11,776	333,747
95	366,689	48,637	11,776	403,550
96	401,614	66,713	43,249	425,078
97	511,236	53,636	140,116	424,756
98	644,504	53,099	229,445	468,158
99	757,315	27,369	341,202	443,482
1900	645,432	30,170	208,732	466,870

Source : Y. Ando, 1975, 77.

lished already in the Edo period and after the Meiji Restoration developed rapidly by the elimination of the feudal power and the recognition of the property rights over farmland by the new government. At the beginning of the Meiji period, the base of Japanese industry was agriculture. Therefore the great part of financing the new government originated from the land tax on the landowner class. This finance was used mainly to sponsor Japanese factories just like European and American models. On the other hand, the landowner class changed directly the land rent rice the capital of industrial sector by buying their shares. At that time the average farm size was about 1 hectare, and that land generally was operated at a low level of productivity. Nonethless more than 50% of a farmer's rice production was required to pay the land rent. Therefore farmers were obliged to rely on cash earning from sericulture and addionally to depend on a portion of wages of their daughters or sons

TABLE 13 CHANGE OF TAXES IN JAPAN, 1875-1928 (Average OF FIVE YEARS) (%)

	Land Tax	Commerce & Industry Tax	Consumption Tax	Income & Inheritance Taxes	Custom	The Other	Total
1875-1879	80.5	3.1	7.9	—	4.3	4.2	100.0
1880-1884	65.6	4.4	21.8	—	4.4	3.8	100.0
1885-1889	69.4	3.8	20.2	0.7	5.2	1.4	100.0
1890-1894	74.3	2.7	17.2	1.1	4.4	0.3	100.0
1895-1899	58.1	5.5	27.2	1.9	7.2	0.1	100.0
1900-1904	32.5	6.8	43.3	5.7	11.7	—	100.0
1905-1909	28.1	9.8	38.2	10.0	13.9	—	100.0
1910-1914	21.8	10.1	40.5	11.4	16.2	—	100.0
1915-1919	16.1	10.9	38.5	22.8	11.7	—	100.0
1920-1924	9.0	10.6	41.6	26.7	12.1	—	100.0
1928	7.4	11.3	39.4	25.8	15.7	—	100.0

Source : H. Ouchi, 1946, 385.

working in the newly developing industrial sector. The high land rent made the life of tenant farmers miserable, and it obliged their daughters or sons to work for low wages in the industrial sector. That is to say the capitalists benifited from both capital and labor from the agricultural sector, while the landowers were able to take the high land rent and to invest very profitably in the industrial sector. Thus in Japan, the bilateral system of capitalist and landowner classes economically reinforced each other very profitably (Table 13).

Next, I wish to describe the characteristics of the Japanese industrial revolution. In the English industrial revolution small factories developed into large factories rapidly, while in the German industrial revolution, large factories rapidly displaced home-manufactured products from the market, but in Japanese case, large government-sponsored industries and home-productions by handcraft existed together. The reason is that in a non-competitive division of the market, large factories mainly produced weapons and cotton thread, while home-productions by handcraft produced clothing, ceramics, tea and so on. After WW-I, small home-industries were converted to factory-productions mainly due to the introduction of electricity and cheap machines. At that time large factories rapidly became monopoly cartels. From the beginning of the world crisis in 1929, small factories tended to become submanufacturers of the large monopoly cartels. The cartels pattern of production was severely disrupted by the defeat of Japan in WW-II, but the same pattern of industrial production persisted and went into a phase of renewed rapid expansion from 1960.

(3) The Rural Community

In the Edo period, the feudal lords calculated all kinds of village production in rice, and on the basis of the total amount of rice for each village determined the percentage of the rice crop to be proffered as tax every year. The unit for paying the rice tax was not the individual farmer, but the village itself. Therefore cooperation and interconnectedness in the rural community was very strong. The Meiji government destroyed this interconnectedness by changing the tax system, i. e., the individual landowners became responsible for paying the land tax. Thus the Meiji government effectively established the landowner class as the centre of the new rural community. After WW-I, tenant disputes became increasingly frequent due to increasing agricultural productivity and the influence of the Soviet Revolution. Japanese agriculture was affected drastically by the world crisis from 1929. In spring 1930, the price of silk cocoons was reduced to half of what it was in the previous year due to fact that silk market in America, the primary silk importer from Japan, collapsed rapidly, as the American depression progressed. The prices of all Japanese agricultural goods plummeted, and those levels of prices were not again attained during the following ten years. Consequently many tenant farmers could not pay their land rents, and the power of the landowner class was greatly reduced. Therefore the government reestablished a new rural community by admitting a group of poor tenants as a corporate member into the agricultural industrial cooperative which had been previously sponsored by the government for the benefit of the landowners and the prosperous farmers. Directly after WW-II, all fields of the landowners if they did not live in their villages and ones over 5 hectares if they lived in their villages were distributed amongst all the tenants, thus establishing a large class of peasant proprietors, and the rural community was reconstructed again by the leading role of new peasant proprietors. Thus it can be seen that the Japanese rural community was reconstructed three time from 1800 to the present time.

(4) Agricultural Technology

Japanese agriculture developed rapidly after the Meiji Restoration to the present time, particularly the average hulled-rice yield for 1 hectare increased from 1700kg to 5000kg. The national and prefectural administrations established the agricultural colleges and experimental stations to develop agriculture.

THE DEVELOPMENT OF TRADITIONAL AGRICULTURE IN THE FIRST HALF OF THE MEIJI ERA

The small scale of farms (about 1 hectare on the average) and the intensive use of labour have been characteristic of Japanese agriculture since the 17th and 18th centuries. In feudal Japan, the development of agriculture was hampered by the various restrictions of the feudal lords. For example, the farmers could not determine the kind of crops to plant ; they were restrained in their purchase and sale of land ; and, because they had to give up the greater part of the crop as land tax to the feudal lords, they had inadequate capital for investments to imporve agriculture. In spite of this, agriculture developed steadily over the period, especially after the 18th century, when development was accelerated by the expansion of commerce.

With the removal of these feudal restrictions after the Meiji Restoration (1868), agriculture, and especially rice cultivation, developed more rapidly. But the way had already been paved for this in feudal times. Measures already taken included comparative experiments on varieties of rice, variety selection and exchange between different districts ; land improvement and manuring ; the practice of harvesting two crops a year ; and the publication of agricultural books (Furushima 1949 : Chapter 6 and Yasuda 1952 : 1-5).

TABLE 14 RICE YIELDS OBTAINED BY LEADING
FARMERS OF JAPAN, *CIRCA* 1889

Prefecture	Name	Yield in about 1889 (*koku per tan*)[a]	Average Yield in Prefecture 1899 (*koku per tan*[a])
Fukushima	K. Okonogi	2.4-2.5	1.14
Ibaragi	S. An	2.6	1.25
Chiba	S. Nara	8.2	2,89
Niigata	T. Katagiri	7.6	2.54
Gifu	S. Hirayama	5.2	1.49
Aichi	K. Ezaki	1.8-2.0	
Aichi	K. Ota	4.0	
Osaka	H. Takaishi	1.7-2.5	
Shimane	S. Iwatsuki	4.6	1.26
Yamaguchi	K. Watanabe	3.5	
Kochi	K. Okazaki	2.4-2.5	
Saga	Ch. Tobimatsu	6.8	2.28
Kumamoto	S. Takeuchi	3.0	

[a] 1 tan=0.1 hectare (approximately) and 1 koku=150 kilograms.
Source : Saito 1968 : 290.

Naozo Nakamura (1819-1882), for example, collected
many varieties of rice from almost all parts of Japan (of
which in 1882 he recognised more than 700 as being
especially excellent). He cultivated them in his own
fields, selected the best, and undertook to spread them
throughout Japan. Such outstanding farmers were able
to obtain a much higher yield of rice than the average at
that time (Table 14).

These leading farmers' techniques of rice cultivation
were based not on European and American agricultural
science, but on their experiences alone.

THE INTRODUCTION OF EUROPEAN AND
AMERICAN AGRICULTURAL SCIENCE
IN THE FIRST HALF OF THE MEIJI ERA

Role of Central Government

After the Meiji Restoration, the government made a concerted effort to introduce European and American agricultural science into Japan. It published translations of
European and American agricultural books. It established a European and American agricultural implement
station and nursery for new crops introduced from
Europe and America at Tsukiji in Tokyo in 1872. This
was removed to Shinjuku in Tokyo in the following year,
and expanded into an experimental station. A branch
was subsequently established at Mita in Tokyo in 1877,
and another, an olive and grape garden, was opened in
Kobe in Hyogo Prefecture in 1879. In 1875, a sheep
ranch was established at Sanrijuka in Chiba Prefecture.

The most important measure of all was the establishment of agricultural schools. In 1872, Hokkaido-Kaitakushi (the Agency for Development of Hokkaido) established at Shiba in Tokyo a school for the development of
Hokkaido, which in 1875, was removed to Sapporo, Hokkaido, and was named Sapporo Nogakko (Sapporo Agricultural School). In later years, this became the Agricultural Department of modern-day Hokkaido University.
Hokkaido, the most northern part of Japan, was scarcely
developed in feudal times and was properly developed
only after 1868.

Komaba Nogakko (Komaba Agricural School) had the
largest influence on the agriculture of the main island of
Honshu. It was expanded into the Agricultural Department of what is now Tokyo University.

At the Komaba School a two years' preparatory course
and three years' regular course, and also a three years'
practical course were offered. The regular course was

171

TABLE 15 FAMILY RANK OF STUDENTS OF THE
KOMABA AGRICULTURAL SCHOOL OF
JAPAN, 1877-8

	Family Rank	Preparatory Course	Agricultural Course	Veterinary Course	Practical Course	Total
The first graduates	Samurai	22	19	27	19	87
(admitted in 1877)	Others	5	1	2	9	17
	Total	27	20	29	28	104
The second graduates	Samurai	8	18	22	6	54
(admitted in 1878)	Others	1	1	1	0	3
	Total	9	19	23	6	57

Source : Iinuma 1969a : 5.

divided into an agricultural course and a veterinary course to which an agricultural chemistry course was soon added. The preparatory course was opened to boys 13-15 years old, the agricultural course to boys 16-18 years old, the veterinary course to boys 16-20 years old, and the practical course to men 20-30 years old.

The regular course was opened to all men, but for the practical course, admission was limited to men who had their own fields and practised agriculture. Initially, however, almost all the students of Komaba School were Samurais (Table 15) and, being of Samurai outlook, they respected the study of theories, but held the practice of agriculture in contempt. This outlook controlled Japanese agricultural scholarship for a long time.

The first five teachers of Komaba School were all Englishmen and lectured on English agricultural science which bore no relation to Japanese agriculture of that time. Their lectures were therefore almost useless for Japanese farmers. They were not reappointed on the expiration of their contract in about 1881, and were replaced by German teachers. These German teachers concerned themselves mainly with Japanese soils and manu-

TABLE 16 AGRICULTURAL SCHOOLS IN JAPAN, 1882

Name	Prefecture	Year Founded	Years of Education	Teachers	Students
Government					
Niigata Kannojyo	Niigata	1875	3	4	19
Nogyo Denshujyo	Ishikawa	1877	3	9	43
Gifu Nogakko	Gifu	1878	4	9	36
Nogakko	Hiroshima	1879	3	5	32
Fukuoka Nogakko	Fukuoka	1880	3	7	38
Kooriyama Nogakko	Fukushima	1880	3	3	22
Nogakko	Tottori	1881	2	1	19
Nogyo Koshujyo	Yamanashi	1882	3	3	15
Private					
Gakunosha Nogakko	Tokyo	1875	5	8	80
Jyui-Gakko	Tokyo	1881	3	8	13
Oharino Nogakko	Akita	1881	2	1	12

Source : Iinuma 1969a : 25.

res, and their lectures proved to be very useful. They studied for a long time in Japan (e. g. Oscar Kerner 1881 -92, Max Fesca 1882-94) and were responsible for the establishment of agricultural chemistry in Japan. Under their influence Komaba School became the centre for the study of and education in Japanese agricultural science, and agricultural chemistry has played a central role in the development of Japanese agricultural science (Iinuma 1969a : 1-24 and Tsukuba 1959 : 143-64).

Role of Local Authorities

Imitating the central government, local authorities (pre-

173

TABLE 17 **THE SUBJECT MATTER OF STUDENT NOTEBOOKS OF THE FUKUOKA AGRICULTURAL SCHOOL, *CIRCA* 1886**

Science		Agricultural Science	
Physics	1	Cultivation	8
Classification of plants	2	Rotation of crops	1
Plant physiology	1	Soils	4
Classification of animals	4	Improvement of soils :	
Animal physiology	2	agricultural implements	1
Geology	1	Forestry	1
Inorganic chemistry	6	Livestock	3
Organic chemistry	9	Livestock pathology	1
		Silkworm : bee	1
		Poultry	1
		Rural economics	1
		Horticulture	1
Total	26	Total	23

Source : Iinuma 1969a : 58.

fectural, town and village) also established agricultural shools and experimental stations (Table 16). For example, Fukuoka Nogakko (Fukuoka Agricultural School) was established by the Fukuoka Prefetural Office in 1879. This school was open to men of 15-25 years, and offered a three years' course. There were about ten teachers, all of whom were Japanese. One half of them lectured in science and the other half in agricultural science. Among them were two Komaba graduates, who played leading roles. According to the reminiscences of one of the first graduates of Fukuoka School, the teachers lectured on European and American agricultural science, so the lectures bore no relation to the agriculture of Fukuoka Prefecture.

The author recently discovered the notebooks of these students, apparently written in 1886. Twenty six volumes

174

were on science and twenty-three on agricultural science
(Table 17). The large number of notebooks concerned
with chemistry in the science category seem to have been
characteristic of the Komaba School (Iinuma 1969a : 25-
61 and Susuda 1970 : 15-27).

Rono Period

As indicated above, these agricultural schools and experimental stations established by the government and
local authorities were of small relevance to the existing
Japanese agriculture and most were abolished in about
1887, as a consequence of the financial stringency of the
time.

In their place, the government and local authorities
employed *ronos* (meaning leading farmers) who acted as
leaders in agriculture for about fifteen years (about 1880-
95) throughout the country. It was during the '*rono*
period', that graduates of both the surviving national
agricultural schools (Sapporo and Komaba) made concerted efforts to Japanize the European and American
agricultural science taught in these two schools ; that is,
to place the *ronos*' proven techniques of rice cultivation on
a scientific base with the aid of the European and American teachings.

For example, Tokiyoshi Yokoi (1860-1927), a Samurai
with no prior knowledge of agriculture, graduated from
the Komaba School in 1880 and was employed at the
Fukuoka School in 1882. He taught there until the clo-
sure of this school in 1887. From notebooks made by
students of his lectures (*circa* 1886), it was clear that he
had a regard for both the agricultural scholars' theories of
feudal Japan and the leading farmers' techniques (see
Appendix B). Fukuoka Prefecture where he lived was
agriculturally the most progressive part of Japan at that
time. In the Fukuoka School, he examined these traditional theories and techniques in the light of European

175

and American agricultural science. As a result of this, he succeeded in Japanizing the foreign agricultural science. For example, he invented the 'ensuisen' (the method of selection of rice seeds by salt water), which was invented following the experiment of Prof Arthur H. Church of Royal Agricultural College in Cirencester of England. On the other hand, he did not blindly follow traditional theories and techniques. Afterwards, he became a professor of the Agricultural Department of Tokyo University (Iinuma 1969a : 603 - 945 ; Tsukuba 1959 : 138 - 56 and Saito 1968 : 260-85).

Meiji System

The unity between the traditional practices and theories and foreign agricultural science became the basis for the new method of rice cultivation which evolved in the second half of the Meiji era and was called the Meiji system. The spread of the Meiji system led to substantial development of rice cultivation and expansion of production.

In 1893, the national experimental station was established at Nishigahara in Tokyo on this new basis and subsequently government and local authorities established agricultural schools and experimental stations of a new type. Almost all of them still remain today. From that time, however, the *rono's* leadership rapidly lost its influence, and Japanese agricultural scholars paid little attention either to the agricultural scholars' theories of feudal Japan or to the farmers' techniques which held sway in the *rono* period (Saito 1968 : 287-96 and Tsukuba 1959 : 153-64).

Many people held this view because they thought that the modern agricultural techniques of these stations excelled the traditional techniques. We have investigated both techniques, and can see that the traditional techniques compared quite well the techniques of the stations. Why

176

were the traditional techniques defeated by the stations' techniques ?

During the industrial and agricultural revolution (the end of the 19th and the beginning of the 20th centuries) cities and countries experienced a shortage of hands. The stations made efforts to save labor in agriculture, but the traditional techniques did not make efforts to save labor in getting best products. This was the reason why the traditional techniques were defeated by the stations. At the present time, however, the stations' techniques have resulted in the threat of agricultural pollution to health by the use of many chemical manures and medicines to save labor. On the other hand, the traditional techniques have survived in villages, and efforts are being made to turn the stations' fragmentary techniques into the useful synthetic techniques, which, at the present time, can be considered organic techniques for opposing agricultural pollution.

FIVE

The Curious Crisis in
Japanese Agriculture

An exceedingly curious form of crisis faces Japan's agriculture at the present time. During the agricultural crisis of the 1930s the farming population was destitute; in the northeast, in particular, there was a long period when the the children could be given no lunch to take to school and the girls were sold off. Now, to the contrary, the farming communities appear at first sight to be extremely prosperous. Homes are well provided with electrical appliances like washing machines, refrigerators and color television, the farmers have their automobiles and not a few have rebuilt their houses. Even so, the farmers have lost faith in the future of agriculture. How can this be?

(1) The Policy of So-called 'Modernization'

We can think of two basic origins for the contradictory state of affairs described above. One is the traditional way of thinking of the Japanese intelligentsia. Ever since the eighth century, when the nation was organized on the basis of cultural imports from China — in particular her bureaucratic system of administration — Japan's intellectuals have always perceived beyond the seas the example of "advanced countries" the emulation of which they feel should represent the goal of Japan's endeavors in a process which they call "modernization" or "development." Thus, the main qualification of a "leader" in Japan came to consist in the extent of his knowledge of the culture of whatever was the "Most Advanced Country" of the moment (before the Meiji Restoration this was China, thereafter "the West" or, after the Second World War, America). Conversely, the extent of his knowledge of his own country was a minor matter.

After the War the USA has been accepted as the "Most Advanced Country" and it is perhaps, therefore, natural, and certainly in conformity with tradition that when Japan's intelligentsia look at her agriculture, they call for "modernization" and mean thereby "Americanization."

The average area of an American farm is 80 hectares and in mechanization and monocultural farming (one farm-one product) the USA leads the world. On the other hand, the average area of a Japanese farm is one hectare. Ignoring this very obvious and basic difference Japan's intelligentsia (government officials and academics) call for "modernization" through the introduction of large machines and the adoption of monocultural farming methods such as are successful in the USA.

Moreover, after 1960, this way of thinking was adopted as official policy and in the short space of 15 years has succeeded in changing the face of Japanese agriculture. That it was able to do so was because it coincided exactly with the thinking of big business, the current sponsor of the government party, the Liberal-Democrats.

Two epoch-making developments have influenced Japan's agriculture since the War. The first was the introduction of Land Reform after the end of the War in 1945, and the second was the onset in 1960 of the period of rapid economic growth.

From the Meiji Restoration in 1868 to the loss of the War, Japanese politics were dominated by a combination of landowners and bourgeoise (capitalists). The lost War, however, put an end to this system when the land-owning class were deprived of their political influence. Thereafter

179

the will of the bourgeoisie (capitalists) was translated directly into policy. It is true that the Land Reform brought about a social revolution in agricultural communities, but equally so that it inevitably produced the political change we have described. Before the War most of the farmers were tenant farmers ; thereafter almost all owned their own land. In addition it is true that bourgeois ideals of rationalization of farm management were given free rein, compared with prewar days, which was a great improvement ; on the other hand, the new situation contained a fundamental weakness for the agricultural classes in that they were potentially placed entirely at the mercy of the bourgeoisie (big business) who now monopolized the political power. This did not become apparent until 1960, during the period when the nation had not yet fully recovered from the wounds of War, but has very much become the main issue after 1960.

From 1960, which marked the beginning of Japan's period of rapid economic advancement, the Keizai Dōyūkai (Japan Committee for Economic Development), an organization representing "big business," and the Nihon Shōkō Kaigisho (The Japan Chamber of Commerce and Industry) began actively to call for the "modernization" of Japan's agriculture. Their arguments and objectives can be reduced to the following :

1. Whilst self-sufficiency is to some extent desirable, even on the basis of the current degree of reliance on imports, the nation should adopt food policies which do not impose a burden on public finances. In particular, the Government's purchasing price of rice should be kept down to international market levels and if that proves impossible, then rice should be imported. The argument derives from the theory of the international division of labor.

2. The so-called "Modernization of Agriculture," whereby present legal restrictions on the sale of agricultural land

are removed, the present minute scale of agricultural ownership is concentrated into larger units, large-scale mechanization and monocultural practices lead to an increase in productivity in agriculture. This is the "modernization of agriculture" thesis.

One may well ask how it is that these managers of big business were converted into experts in agriculture economy, suddenly, at the outset of the period of rapid economic growth. Where their first point is concerned, they were thinking of reducing fiscal burdens, reducing food prices and at the same time real wages as a means of increasing exports. Where their second point is concerned their objective was the securing of the labor supply necessary to provide the required high rate of economic growth. The application of mechanization to the existing one hectare per unit of average scale of agricultural management must surely release a considerable reserve of labor. The trend would surely be accelerated by encouraging a monocultural agricultural econmy. In these circumstances if attention were paid to the raising of industrial wages rather than the price of agricultural products then labor could be expected to move from agriculture into factories and other industrial work sites just as water flows downhill.

Since these views on the part of "big business" (aimed at the Government, the Liberal-Democratic Party and the country in general) coincided perfectly with those of the intelligentsia (government officials and academics), "modernization" or "Americanization" of agriculture was promptly adopted as official policy. In the mere 15 years since the initiation of this policy in 1960 the results have been : 1. national self-sufficiency in agricultural production has fallen to 71 per cent. Most remarkable are such figures (as of 1972) as 38 per cent for compounding materials for animal feed, 5 per cent for wheat, and 3 per cent for soybeans. 2. Mechanization and monoculture has become the rule. By January 1972 those farming house-

181

holds engaged solely in farming had fallen to 14.4 per cent of the total. At the same time economic growth proceeded on an amazing scale and at a fast tempo, only comparable to the scale and speed of that of West Germany.

The farming community supplied its labor to big business in factories and other work places, and in order to provide more time for such work on a part-time or "temporary basis" increasingly adopted the use of machinery, fertilizers and agricultural chemicals, adding to the profits of their manufacturers. All this had the effect of increasing the cost and prices of agricultural products and assisted in promoting export of manufactured products. International trade is the exchange of products between countries. In order to sell manufactured exports abroad it is necessary to buy from abroad agricultural products or industrial raw materials.

The Government and the Liberal-Democratic Party began to call for increased import from overseas of agricultural products — with the exception of rice which comes under a food control system. This, they said, would ensure constantly increasing exports of manufactured goods.

The unusual weather conditions which appeared two years ago and continued last year have combined with steep increases in ocean freight rates to produce worldwide food shortages. This has persuaded the Ministry of Agriculture from April of this year to concentrate its attention on the increasing of agricultural output. However, other leading food-producing countries have also embarked on policies of increasing production (the USA, for instance, in January this year abolished all restrictions on agricultural production, and replaced them with price support programs for the principal products). In Japan, however, the Government continues with its big-business-orientated policies and makes no attempt to modify its support of the international division of labor thesis. For instance, in November of last year Prime Minister Tanaka ordered the conversion of 300,000 hectares of agricultural land in January of this year he invited the Philippines to aim at making itself a food-supplying base for Japan. In such circumstances it is a little difficult to guess where the Ministry of Agriculture's new production-increase policy is supposed to lead.

The home of the international divion of labor theory is England. The Industrial Revolution began some 200 years ago in England and that country began to supply the world with cheap and good quality manufactures. In order to prevent the development of manufacturing in other countries Britain called for free trade in, and no imposition of import duties on manufactured goods. In return Britain imposed no duties at all on the food products it imported from other countries.

Eventually, however, industrial output increased in the USA, Germany, France and, finally Japan, and Britain found it increasingly difficult to export its manufactures. Even so, she continued to cling to the theory of the international division of labor. She, thus, sacrificed her agriculture in order to foster and protect her manufacturing industry and agriculture went into decline. As a result, British agriculture, at one time the most advanced in Western Europe, abandoned the highly productive system of mixed farming (an organic combination or arable and livestock farming) and replaced it with either extensive monocultural farming or the production of poultry and livestock on the basis of import of cheap feeds from abroad. Without doubt one of the principal sources of Britain's economic problems at this time is the imbalance in overseas trade resulting from a standstill in exports of manufactured goods combined with increases in imports of agricultural products.

Looking at recent developments in Japanese agriculture one gets the feeling that it has been subjected in the short space of 15 years to a process which continued in Britain

183

over a period of 100 years. Surely, if the Japanese Government persists in its present subscription to the theory of the international division of labor, then this will bring about not only the collapse of Japan's agriculture, but a decline in the economy as a whole.

(2) Toward a modern Mixed Farming

The policies the Government has pursued for the last 15 years with the object of "modernization" of Japan's agriculture have in fact had an adverse effect from the point of view of true rationalization.

Truly rational agricultural management aims at maximum utilization of available land, labor and materials so as to produce no waste of resources. The validity of this statement is more readily recognizable if we think in terms of a company or factory. If the manager achieved inadequate utilization of his labor or materials he would be a failure and his company would quickly go out of business. If we consult agricultural literature of the Tokugawa era we find everywhere a repetition of this idea that success follows only a maximum utilization of available land, labor and material resources.

For instance, if we compare the *Aizu Nōshō*, published in 1684, with the Agricultural Calendar produced in 1972 by agricultural authorities in the same region, Fukushima Prefecture, we have to immediately admit that the former is ahead in its ideas about effective, rationalized farm econmy. The reason for this is clearly that present-day agriculture has completely abandoned the mixed farming which is the true and only basis for effective farm management. After 1960, the Ministry of Agriculture has deployed an enormous budget in order to lay the foundations for "modernization" of agriculture ; instead it has had the effect of destroying the very foundations for the rationalization of farming.

To quote a further example we would cite the *Nōgyō*

184

Zensho (Complete Book of Agriculture) published in 1697 and recognized as the most authoritative of the many treatises published in the Tokugawa era. In its introduction, it contains the following injunction, "In tilling the land many different matters have to be borne in mind. Firstly, the farmer must appreciate his own limitations before working the fields and paddies. It is best always to work well within the limit of his capacity. He should never work beyond his limit."

Translating this into modern terms, rather than aiming at extensive farming with mechanized labor on the American model, the traditional nature of Japanese farming indicates that higher rewards can be obtained by working "within the limit" by an intensive rather than extensive use of labor resources.

The above quotation from the Complete Book of Agriculture is in fact a quotation from the introduction to the 6th volume "Farming" of the Nung Cheng Ch'üan Shu, an authoritative Chinese treatise published in 1639. This in turn is a quotation from the *Ch'i-min-yao-shu* published in Shantung Province somewhere around the middle of the sixth century.

Thus, the intensive feature of Japanese agriculture is not peculiar to Japan but applies to the whole of East Asia, it is not a feature which applied merely in the past, but is significant in the present and for the future — as long as agriculture continues to be practiced in East Asia.

Thus we can see that agricultural policy over the last 15 years, taking as it does America as its model and calling for "modernization" via increase in scale, mechanization and monoculture, has in fact completely ignored what is the basic feature of Japanese agriculture. In Part I Chapter 2, I examined the reasons for basic differences between American and Japanese agriculture or between East Asian and European American agriculture.

The climatic elements which exert most influence on the nature of a region's agriculture are rainfall and temperature. In studying these elements, we have seen that the historical development of Western and Eastern Agriculture have contained great differences. Thus, agriculture in the relatively dry regions developed through the extensive use of labor (mechanization) and in the direction of large management units. These have reached their greatest degree of development in the case of USA agriculture.

On the other hand, in the humid regions, particularly where summer temperatures are high and land productivity similarly high, the trend was toward the more intensive utilization of labor rather than otherwise. This type of agriculture has reached its highest degree of development in Japan. By the measures of production per unit of area and degree of control exerted over the natural environment, the respective agricultural systems of the USA and Japan undoubtedly, in their different ways, lead the world.

From ancient times, and, certainly, if we judge from agricultural treatises written from the 17th century onwards, Japanese agriculture has developed as a type of mixed farming based on the labor of the family; this is because such a system was one most suited to hoeing-type agriculture. We have already seen how the "modernization" policies adopted since 1960 have tried to deny this.

Nevertheless, whilst, in general, mixed farming in Japan has been wiped-out, still a few instances have survived in each district in some seemingly miraculous fashion. Similarly, whilst almost no farmer can by now continue to exist on income from farming alone, the few remaining examples of mixed farming appear to be making a very good living at it.

To introduce an example, we may take the Y. family in Hyōgo prefecture. The work force consists basically of two brothers, who work 30 milk cows, 12 calves, 1.2 hectares of Paddy, 1 hectare of dry arable land, and 500 poultry, their whole operation being highly mechanized. For instance, the cows are milked mechanically and the cow-sheds are equipped with electrically-operated conveyors which automatically take straw and manure from the sheds to a small truck. This conveys these materials to the fields where they represent fertilizer for the production of vegetables and feed beet. Similarly the refuse left after vegetables are shipped to market represents valuable feed for the animals. The feature of the mechanical equipment used is that it is suited to the 2.2 hectare size of the farm. The tractor, for instance, develops 17 horsepower.

This type of small scale mechanization allows the adoption of a variety of types of farming, each of which assists the other. In contrast, in a monocultural type farming operation, like milk-production, there is not only no means of using the manure produced by the cows, but its very disposal is a costly matter. As a fertilizer used in production of vegetables it represents a valuable asset. Similarly low grade vegetables have virtually no economic value in the market, but provide very welcome feed for milk cows. Thus, through maximization of the degree of utilization of labor, land and materials it is possible to lower unit production costs and make a handsome living.

This type of modern mixed farming making optimal use of small machines surely represents a highly suitable future style for Japan's agriculture. It would require a minimum size of one hectare per farm in areas the west of Kantō and 3 to 5 times that the east of Kantō, whilst in terms of maximum size and on the basis of provision of labor in principle from the family and of present levels of technology it is unlikely that in West Japan farms could be larger than five hectares in area. This is exactly contrary to the thesis of the intelligentsia (government officials and academics) who maintain that the larger the farm the more efficient it is.

What, then, are we to do with those farms less than

one hectare in size ? Since they cannot do it on their own, then a number of units engaging in monoculture farming should be encouraged to join together in a cooperative form of modern mixed farming. In this case accounts would have to be kept on the basis of one cooperative unit.

The real task for the future is to ensure that these mere dots on the map which represent the present miraculously-surviving examples of successful mixed farming are converted into whole areas on the map. In the first place, to establish such examples of modern mixed farming will call for finance on a large scale.

On the other hand, however much agricultural efficiency is raised, the efforts of the farmers to reduce costs will merely fill the pockets of the middlemen if the distribution system remains as inefficient as at present, when a cucumber sold by a producer for ¥2 can cost as much as ¥40 by the time it reaches the consumer.

In connection with these problems of finance and the distribution system, it surely is incumbent on the Agricultural Cooperative Movement, with its monster organization throughout the nation, to take the lead. But the Nōkyō (the agricultural cooperatives) at present seems to have divorced itself from agricultural production and to be concerning itself either with the purchase of rice as agent of the Government or with the sale to the agricultural communities of manufactured goods such as automobiles and television sets. It must revert to its original tasks.

At the same time, if these problems of finance and distribution are to be resolved, the Government also must modify the current policy which serves the interests of business, and replace it with one which fosters both agriculture and industry and maintains a proper balance between the interests of the two. This is needed not only to save Japan's agriculture but to ensure the future health of the economy as a whole.

*   *   *

[**A Postscript**] This chapter was described in 1975. After that time, Japanese agriculture has been declined more rapidly. In regard to this matter, please see next Chapter.

SIX

How Agricultural Products are unfit for Human Consumption in Japan recently

The other day I went to see a play entitled *A Primer for Japan's Prosperity*. In one scene two women who look like housewives lived in a danchi (housing complex) go to a farmhouse in order to buy vegetables that have been grown without the use of chemicals. They tell the farmer that if he will supply them with "safe" vegetables on a long-term basis, they are willing to sign a contract. This is what is referred to as direct producer-to-consumer sales.

So-called direct sales originally grew out of a desire on the part of the consumer to eliminate the middlemen, including wholesaler and grocery store, so he could obtain cheaper vegetables. Now the problem is no longer price, but availability of produce that is safe to eat. People still do not think of direct selling as an antigovernment protest movement, however, and it is this lack of a clear political awareness that is causing direct sales to falter or fail completely.

Why is it that the vegetables on the market these days have all been grown with chemical fertilizers, have in most cases been picked and crated before they are ripe, and are dangerous, tasteless and expensive? In other words, why do we get produce that is unfit for human consumption? The answer is to be found in our political structure — the same stucture that gave us the Lockheed political scandal.

About thirty years ago, when the Japanese economy had embarked upon a period of rapid growth, the major business organizations, Keidanren (Federation of Economic Organizations), Keizai Dōyūkai (Committee for Economic Development), and Nihon Shōkō Kaigisho (Japan Chamber of Commerce and Industry), offered many suggestions concerning the modernization of agriculture in Japan. Their proposals covered a wide area, but, as stated above, really boiled down to two points of view. One is the agricultural modernization theory, according to which the best way to modernize agriculture is to replace the existing small farmer who grows a variety of items with large scale single-crop operations. The second is the theory of comparative advantage, which holds that it is more efficient to import inexpensive produce from overseas than to grow it at home.

The real motives which prompted the business world to make such proposals at the same time it was trying to initiate rapid economic growth were quite pragmatic. Those who favored the agricultural modernization theory wanted to get workers off the farms and into the cities where they were badly needed for the development of the economy. The proponents of the theory of comparative advantage, on the other hand, believed that the more agricultural products Japan imported from a country the better the chances of using that country as a market for its manufactured goods.

In 1961 the government, under the control of the Liberal Democratic party, legislated these suggestions into law by enacting the Fundamental Law on Agriculture, thereby laying the foundation for all subsequent agricultural policy. In the last fifteen years Japan's agriculture has become almost exclusively "monocultural," or single-crop, mechanized cultivation. At the same time the percentage of the total number of fulltime farmers has dropped sharply from 34 percent to 11 percent, and Japan's rate of real self-sufficiency has plummeted from 80 per-

191

cent to 40 percent.

In recent years large numbers of Japanese farmers have switched to single-crop operations in an effort to free as many hours as possible for work in factories or other jobs. They have made extensive use of agricultural chemicals including fertilizers and insecticides, and as a result are producing foodstuffs that are dangerous to eat. They have also had to invest large sums of money in machines and other equipment which they use only a few times a year, so with soaring costs they are finding themselves unable to compete in the international market. Thus, they are contributing to the liberalization of import restrictions on agricultural commodities other than rice, and in turn, to the growth of industry.

This monoculture, which is endorsed by the Ministry of Agriculture necessitates transporting goods great distances and hastens the expansion of related marketing organizations, such as the agricultural cooperatives (Nōkyō). The Mihistry of Agriculture, in fact, now calls long-distance shipping by large cooperatives the truly "modern way," and has actively encouraged developments in that direction.

The notion that transporation to and from remote areas can be a profitable undertaking, however, is pure myth. Prices are set by the market, and in the end it is the market which profits and the producer who suffers. Furthermore, the bigger an agricultural cooperative grows the more bureaucratic it becomes, and the more impersonal the relationship between its administrators and members (the farmers) is. The ones who are glad about growing bureaucratization are the central and regional government officials and the national Nōkyō leaders. The reason is that the more bureaucratic the organization becomes the easier it is to "guide" the branch offices scattered throughout the country.

The original purpose of the coops was to serve the interests of the farmers, not the bureaucracy, and the only way that can be achieved is through a personal relationship between the Nōkyō personnel and the farmers. When a coop grows beyond three hundred households it is safe to say that it can no longer perform its original mission.

The same is true of direct sales. If there is no face-to-face contact between consumer and producer, such agreements are doomed to failure. In one sense the most important job of the coop is to foster this personal contact. Direct sales cannot possibly succeed when linked to mass production of single items, long-distance transportation and cooperatives with mammoth bureaucracies.

Therefore, the real key to success in this area is to be found in production and consumption on a regional basis with small-scale cooperatives consisting of farmers who raise a smaller quantity of several different items. After all, if we cannot get a large number of agricultural products shipped in every day, how can we possibly escape our dependence on the markets and grocery stores? Moreover, it is precisely when the producer and the consumer know each other and deal face-to-face that we will be able to exchange the present "dangerous-to-your-health" produce for merchandise grown with organic fertilizer instead of chemicals, allowed to ripen naturally, in addition to being safe, delicious and cheap.

Consumers should not forget, however, how difficult it is for farmers to carry on small-scale multicrop operations. For those who practice monoculture there are funds available from both the government and the cooperatives. For the small independent farmer, however, there is nothing. Unless the consumer is prepared to support this kind of independent multiple-crop business all the way, the producer-to-consumer method will not be successful. Thus, direct sales is a protest movement directed at the ruling Liberal Democratic party and its persistent overemphasis on industry. Likewise, it is a catalyst for an immediate, concrete, antigovernment movement which will bring together various other interest groups — the citizens' (antipollution) organizations, the labor movement, and the farmers' groups, all of whom are plagued by politics of and for big business.

During the recent 30 years, Japanese agriculture has declined rapidly, for example, the self-sustenance ratio of grains has dwindled from 82% in 1960 to 32% in 1984. Now there are very few successors of farmers and very few brides for farmers. Recently I surveyed the farmers throughout Japan, and could find three common conditions for active farmers who have successors and brides. (1) They carry out multiple farming. (2) They are small family farmers. (3) Their marketings are direct farmer-to-consumer sales. On the other hand, the agricultural policy of the Japanese Government has promoted since 1961, (1) mono-culture of rice cultivation, (2) large farmers as an enterprice, (3) traffic marketing of large quantity by mono and large scale agriculture.

We can see that the agricultural policy of the Japanese Government has strongly opposed active farmers during the 30 years. Multiple farming is the traditional Japanese agriculture, and mono-culture is opposed to it. In general, agriculture is developed by modernization based on tradition, and declines by modernization opposed to tradition. It is difficult to carry out original and creative management in the small rice mono-culture (its average farm size is 1 ha,), but in the multiple farming, even if a farm is 1 ha., farmers can have many chances of original and creative management of their farms. If farmers can not have chances of original and creative management, they are liable to lose interest in such farm management. It is for this reason that many farmers in rice mono-culture have lost interest in agriculture.

The traffic marketing of large quantity as a result of the mono and large scale agriculture is controled by large markets of cities, and often troubled with the frequent changes of prices of agricultural products, and has lost the intimate relation with nearby towns. But by multiple farming many kinds of agricultural products are naturally produced, which is a disadvantage compared to large markets based on the auction system of the mono and large quantity of agricultural products. Therefore, its marketing has become direct farmer-to-consumer Sales, and farmers are saved from the strong control of large markets of cities and can keep the intimate relation between farmers and nearby towns.

At the present time, the Japanese Government appears reluctant to change the agricultural policy, that is, the mono and large farming policy, because of the need of support of enterprises which for the import of agricultural products from foreign countries and the export of industrial products to the same countries. But if the Japanese Government changes its policy, and the promotion of the rice mono-culture is ceased and traditional farming is encouraged, Japanese agriculture will soon be revived.

SEVEN

Agriculture and Preservation of the Environment
—Outlook of Agriculture in the 21st Century—

In the 21st century, farming and preservation of the environment will be the main concern for agriculture.

In the 20th century, modernization of agriculture which had started in the US, spread all over the world.

It is, of course, desirable that the farmers should be released from hard work through the introduction of machinery. But here, we should keep in mind that this mechanization can be a dangerous factor in the destruction of the environment, breaking a symbiotic relationship between agriculture and livestock.

Everywhere in the world, agriculture has developed according to the climate of each region. The climatic elements which exert the most influence on agricultural regions are humidity and aridity in summer. For example, in regions like the US, where it is dry in summer, the soil productivity is low. Therefore the production of the crops will not make much difference whether the farming is done through intensive or extensive use of labor. Therefore it is reasonable that in such a farming area, in order to obtain larger crops, agriculture needed to be developed in the direction of monoculture with utilization of livestock resources or machine power.

On the other hand, in regions like Japan, Korea and China, where the humidity in summer is high, the soil productivity is high. Thus there is a big difference in crop harvest whether intensive labor is utilized or extensive labor is applied. In this case, agricultural practices developed in the direction of small sized mixed farming with an intensive use of labor rather than a large cultivation by an extensive labor.

Whether it is monoculutural farming or mixed one, for a long time the agriculture has been so called "sustainable agriculture" meaning "in harmony with the natural environment". It has not damaged natural space, but it has helped to protect and preserve it. That is why the agriculture has been able to sustain mankind over a long period of time.

But, it should be noted here, agricutural practices also serve as a function of protecting the environment when land is cultivated and productive. But this positive outcome has been taken for granted.

It is only recently that we have realized the importance of it.

Since the mixed farming depends largely on man power, it has never damaged the natural environment. But, in monocultural farming, as it was said, "without livestock, no agriculture exists," the livestock played an essential part in providing the farming power and food for man.

But this trend changed. In Germany in the first half of the 19th century the study of mineral fertilizer began. In the US, in the latter half of the same century, agricultural machines were developed.

All this weakened the agriculture's dependency on the use of livestock. Consequently, it gave a rise to environmental problems, which was more visible in the US than anywhere else the world. But acutally it was the developing countries that received the most terrible side effects through the introduction of the American type of mechanized monocultural farming methods.

The American government, after the defeat of the Vietnam War (1974), tried to resolve the huge deficit caused by the Vietnam War. Taking advice from the William's

Committee, they sold arms and agricultural products abroad which were the main export items in the US.

As a result, arms exports increased rapidly year after year. It reached $ 14 billion in 1985 compared to $ 900 million in 1970. Though, I will not go further on this data.

The export of crops increased, as well. The total amount of the crops exported in 1984 amounted to $ 33.5 billion. If we take the average figures from 1975 to 1979, America supplied the world with 14% of its wheat, 48% of its corn, and 62% of its soy beans. By the beginning of the 1980s, half of the principal crops in the world were produced in America alone.

In the meantime, the price of crops has risen threefold.

As a result of such an economic boom through exports, the mechanized monocultural agriculture developed with surprising speed, which consequently accelarated concentration of wealth in the farmers community. (If we take an example, the number of farming households and farming population in 1950 were 5.65 million and 9.93 million. Those figures fell in 1973 to 2.67 million and 3.96 million respectively. During the years from 1970 to 1981, 1% of all farmers in the US accounted for 66 % of the total farming households income in the US.)

But 1984 was the peak year for American crop exports.

After that year, due to the recovery of other agricultural countries such as Argentina, and a rise in the dollar's value in America, the crop prices decreased The people who had expanded their management expecting to get big profits through exports went into bankruptcy one after another. To cope with the drop of the crop prices, mechanization and monocultural farming was practiced more than ever, which caused agricultural practices to lose the function of protecting the environment. This without a doubt, led to weaken the recovery in the fertility of the soil. Underground water was polluted and dried up from using a large amounts of water. The soil eroded through the use of chemical fertilizers and agricultural chemicals. All this caused environmental pollution on a large scale.

The American government in order to deal with the worldwide crop price decline gave farmers and some leading export companies subsidies to cover the difference between actual production cost and world crop price.

This put pressure on the American national finance. (For example, the financial deficit was $ 74.4 billion in 1980, $ 221.0 billion in 1980, and $ 250 billion in 1988.)

As I have explained, the American type of agriculture, which is largh-scale monocultural farming with mechanized labor, attracted developing countries very much. They too were trying hastily to modernize their agriculture for the purpose of obtaining foreign currency.

When introducing the modern technology in name of the "Green Revolution" in those cuunties, they denied the existing traditional self-sufficient agriculture. Instead, they adopted monocultural farming and utilized a huge amount of fertillizer and agricultural chemicals. They built irrigation systems on a large scale, and introduced machinery unfit for the farming in those regions. Thus, in many cases all these attempts ended in failure, and only left their countries with a huge national debt. The worst of all was deforestation. Many rain forests were cut down on the pretext of exploiting cultivatable land.

This caused surface soil normally covered with many layers of plants to become bare, and consequently when heavy rainfall occured, the surface soil was easily washed away since it lacked organic substance. It was no longer capable of holding much water. In such a short period, the land became barren and desert.

At present, crops are still over produced on a global level, but we can predict that there will be a worldwide food shortage in the near future and also the destruction of the natural environment will accelerate.

In 1950, the crop production was 630 million tons, and

the world population was 2.5 billion. But in 1993, it was 1.7 billion tons, and 5.5 billion respectively.

The population increase was bigger than that of the crop production. Moreover, the crop production has not risen since the 1980s.

As for the cultivated area, it peaked in 1981. Since then, it has tended to fall. Suppose the population continues to grow at this rate, the present crop supply per person, which is 346 kg, will fall to 248 kg. by the years of 2030.

Under such circumstances, if a certain country in the world keeps importing crops from abroad with its huge economic power supporting it, the rest of the countries will surely criticize that one particular country.

Therefore, in the 21st century it will by no doubt be necessary to promote "Sustainable agriculture". This will aim at both the development of self-sufficient farming and the control of the environmental condition. Here, I would like to show you an example of mechanized agriculture introduced and practiced in China and Japan after the 1960s.

Both the Chinese and Japanese Governments tried to introduce and adopt this American type of agriculture to their countries after the 1960s. In the case of China, when it was introduced, they never dismissed their traditional mixed farming, which was a very wise thing to do. Instead, they modified it to a form of "large scale mixed farming" and the agriculture in China developed promptly to a marvellous degree.

On the other hand, the Japanese government tried to deny its traditional small mixed farming in order to utilize the labor from the farming communities, which was needed to meet the rapid economic growth at that time. But wise Japanese farmers retained their traditional "small-scale management" without expanding the existing one hectre per unit of average scale of agricultural management. Under the government's policy, the Japan's agriculture took a form of "monocultural farming in one hectare area". This is a very unusual process practiced no where in the world. If it had been mixed farming, even with "one hectare", the farmer could have been more creative in their farming practices. But under the government policy of "one hectare monoculture", the farmers lost their incentive in their work and just obeyed the government rules. Consequently agricultural productivity decreased rapidly, but the natural environment was not damaged so much. Since then great efforts have been made on the part of some farmers who have tried to make their farming work through so called "Producer-Consumer Cooperation". With this system they have a direct contact with the consumers. Thanks to these farmers' efforts, the trational small-scale mixed farming has survived up to the present time contrary to the expectation of the government.

From what we have seen, we can conclude the following ; the agriculture will undoubtly develope if the mechanized labor is applied to the traditional agriculture. If, however, the traditional agriculture is denied, the agriculture will surely decline.

Thus, if we intend to modernize agricultural practices and develop "sustainable agriculture" successfully in the 21st century, we must respect the traditonal agriculture of each region.

Under these circumstances, what will draw the world's attention is "Producer-Consumer Cooperation", where a producer goes directly into cooperation with a consumer. This process was brought about at the end of the 20th century so as to sustain and develop the Japanese type of traditional agriculture.

I have traveled throughout Japan and looked for productive and motivated farmers when the agriculture itself has been declying.

Among those farmers, I have found three common points : 1) their farming is mixed, 2) the management scale is small, so that they have enough time to be crea-tive in the process of farming, 3) they are a part of the "Producer-Consumer Cooperation", which supports small scale mixed farming methods.

Contrary to this, since 1961, the Japanese government has called for : 1) monocutural farming, 2) business oriented management, 3) Central Market system through which mass shipment of a single product is possible.

As you can notice, the government's policy contradicts the three conditions found among the active and produc-tive farmers. It's no wonder that Japan's agriculture has rapidly declined since 1961.

As this case in Japan shows, it is obvious that to de-velope "Sustainable Agriculture" in the 21st century, "modernization of agriculture" should be carried out "on the basis of tradition".

Book Review : *Fukuokaken* ed., *Nomushi Gyogyoshi* (Survey of Agricultural and Fishing Implements in *Fukuoka* Prefecture, 1879). *Fukuoka Shiryō* (Materials for the History of Fukuoka Prefecture) Vol. 3. Fukuoka, 1982, 368pp.

After the Meiji Restoration (the end of Japanese feudalism, 1868), the Japanese government was anxious to introduce European and American culture and techniques. The Japanese government attempted to take measures in this direction but did not take into account the real conditions of agriculture and fishing in Japan, and failed to achieve the desired results. As a result in 1882 the Japanese government switched from the policy of introducing European and American culture and techniques to the policy of taking a serious view of the traditional techniques of agriculture and fishing. The author limits his comments to th agricultural aspects.

The scholars who graduated from the national agricultural colleges endeavoured to unite the European and American agricultural theory and the Japanese agricultural techniques, and accomplished their aims about 1893. Since that time, the Japanese scholars have carried out research and education in agriculture based on this new agricultural science. Over the period from 1881 to 1893 (the period of emphasis on traditional agriculture), the central and local governments surveyed the traditional agricultural techniques, especially the agricultural implements. Until recently, the books of survey of the agricultural implements only from 19 prefectures have been recovered.

The oldest of these books is the book of survey of 1879, compiled by Fukuoka local government. It is especially important because the agriculture of Fukuoka prefecture was the most progressive at that time. The original book was painted by brush in color and this book is a copy in color resembling the original. On the first pages, 36 kinds of hoes are shown. At that time, the hoe was the most important agricultural implement, and of course there was also the plough. It seems to have been introduced to Japan from China through Korea in the 7th or 8th century, and since then up to the 19th century the Chinese plough was used by Japanese farmers. North China is in the dry zone, and the Chinese plough had a long sole suitable for this climate, because the long sole prevents deep tillage and presses the surface of the soil to preserve water. In Japan, the hoe was used not only for hoeing but also for deep tillage in place of the plough used in Europe and America. In Japan, during the period from the 16th to 19th centuries, the hoe was developed for deep tillage, and there were many kinds of hoes to suit the various conditions of the soil. Especially the *bicchuguwa* was the most useful hoe for deep tillage, invented in the 17th century and widely used in Japan.

In the following pages, we can see the groups of rakes and spades. Especially interesting is the *ganzume* which has a short wooden helve (about 20cm) and 4 iron teeth for hoeing and weeding. Its using requires a lot of physical strength and training, but hoeing and weeding are done very effectively.

Further, there are shown three kinds of ploughs : a Chinese plough (a long sole plough), a no sole plough and a short sole plough. The no sole plough does not have the sole which prevents deep tillage, so it is possible to till deeply with it, but much physical strengh and training is required. Since the end of the 19th century,

Fig. 59. ILLUSTRATION IN *NOMUSHI GYOGYOSHI*

1.

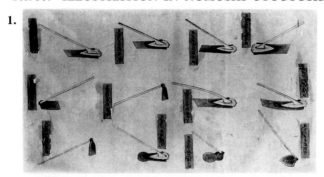

2.

3.

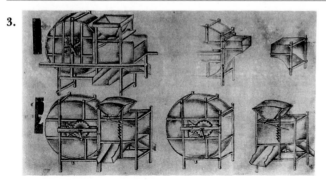

1. hoes   2. ploughs   3. winnowing machines
Source : Fukuokaken 1979, Plate 4, 11, 26.

the no sole plough spread from Fukuoka prefecture
throughout Japan, and became an element of Japanese
agricultural revolution. The short sole plough can be
used more easily for deep tillage than the no sole plough,
so since the beginning of the 20th century it has been in
wide use in Japan. The short sole plough shown in this
book is the original type improved as the modern type.

In the following pages, we can see many kinds of
thrashing tools (*sembakoki, mangokutoshi, uchidana, tomi,*
etc.), thrashing-mill, fail, sickle, harrow, mattock, tub and
winnow. Especially, the *kambei* was a kind of spade used
to scop out mud from ditches, and the water-wheel carried by a farmer was used for paddy field irrigation by
river water.

At the end of this book there are many *emas.* Among
them there are 21 emas for use in agriculture. The *ema* is
a votive tablet offered to the shrine as a token of petition.
These agricultural *emas* were offered to the shrines in the
villages in the 17th to 19th centuries, and the scenes from
agriculture and village life in the 17th to 19th centuries
are painted vividly in color. These are very important
and interesting data enabling a better insight into agriculture and village life at that time.

La Logique Spatiale
de L'agriculture Japonaise

Les politiques mises en oeuvre par le gouvenement japonais au cours des vingt dernières années pour ⟨moderniser⟩ l'agriculture, marquent en réalité un recul selon le point de vue de la tradition. La littérature agricole japonaise remonte à l'époque Tokugawa (XVIᵉ-XIXᵉ siècle), et partout s'y retrouve l'idée selon laquelle la réussite implique une utilisation maximale de la terre, du travail et des ressources matérielles disponibles. Par exemple, le *Nôgyô Zensho*, publié en 1697, et reconnu comme le plus autorisé des nombreux traités de cette époque, contient l'injonction suivante : ⟨En cultivant, il faut considérer plusieurs choses. Premièrement, l'agricultur doit apprécier ses propres limites avant de travailler ses champs et ses rizières. Il est toujours mieux de travailler dans la limite de ses moyens. Il ne faut jamais travailler au-delà de ses limites⟩. Transposé en termes modernes, cela signifie que, plutôt que de viser une agriculture extensive avec travail mécanisé sur le modèle américain, on obtiendra de meilleurs résultats en employant intensivement ses forces de travail. Cette citation du *Nôgyô Zensho* provient en fait du *Nongsheng Quanshu* (⟨traité d'agronomie⟩), un ouvrage apprécié, publié en 1639, et qui s'est à son tour inspiré du *Qimin Yaoshu* (⟨Arts fondamentaux à l'usage des masses⟩) publié en Chine du Nord vers le milieu du VIᵉ siècle.

Le caractère intensif de l'agriculture japonaise n'est pas

particulier au pays, mais concerne toute l'Asie orientale ; et ce n'est pas seulement un trait du passé : il conserve tout son sens dans le présent et le futur — aussi longtemps qu'il y aura une agriculture en Asie orientale.

On voit donc que la politique agricole des vingt dernières années, s'inspirant du modèle américain et prêchant la ⟨modernisation⟩ par le changement d'échelle, la mécanisation et la monoculture, a en fait complètement ignoré les fondements mêmes de l'agriculture japonaise. Nous devons examiner les raisons des différences de fond qui existent entre l'agriculture japonaise et l'agriculture américaine, comme entre celles de l'Europe et de l'Asie orientale.

I. DEUX TYPES DE CULTURES CÉRÉALIÈRES DANS LE MONDE.

Les instuments aratoires employés dans le monde peuvent être divisés en deux catégories : l'une pour les labours superficiels, l'autre pour les labours profonds. La première vise à économiser l'eau du sol (les labours profonds exagèrent les pertes en eau) et la seconde sert surtout à enfouir les mauvaises herbes (le labour superficiel n'y réussit guère). Ces outils ont des buts contradictoires, et sont fort différents dans leur structure même.

On peut naturellement supposer que les premiers sont employés dans la zone sèche, les seconds dans la zone humide. A s'en tenir au classique indice d'aridité de de Martonne, on admettra que la séparation de celles-ci correspond en gros à la valeur 20 (si $i = P/(t+10)$) ; au-dessous de 10, c'est le ⟨désert⟩. Mais ces valeurs annuelles ne sauraient suffire du point de vue de l'agriculture : il faut tenir compte de la répartition saisonnière des précipitations. On peut considére qu'un indice 5 pour le trimestre d'été (juin-août) marque la limite inférieure de la culture des céréales d'été. En combinant l'indice annuel et l'indice estival (tableau 1), on fait apparaître

RÉSUMÉ

TABLEAU 1

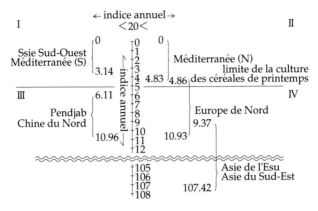

quatre quartiers (pour simplifier, on n'a considéré que l'hémisphère Nord, et en excluant la Russie et l'Amérique).

Le type I correspond à la zone à pluies d'hiver où, la culture de céréales de printemps étant impossible, la terre est en jachère du printemps è l'automne, superficiellement labourée aussi souvent que possible afin de minimiser les pertes en eau (《agriculture à jachère ménageant l'eau》). Les grains sont semés en octobre, les céréales d'hiver profitant des pluies de cette saison. Mais, dans la plus grande partie de la région, partout où l'indice annuel est inféieur à 10, on ne peut cultiver que sous irrigation.

Dans le type II, l'agriculture est de même nature, mais ne dépend plus que des précipitations naturelles : l'indice est supérieur à 20, bien qu'on soit encore en zone sèche.

Le type III groupe notamment la Chine du Nord et le Pendjab, oú l'indice annuel est inférieur à 20 mais où l'indice estival détival dépasse 5. On est en zone sèche, mais les cultures sont dans les champs du printemps à l'automne ; les labours à la charrue sont impossibles pendant les saisons pluvieuses, et on cultive à la houe pour économiser l'eau (《agriculture à la houe ménageant

RÉSUMÉ

Tableau 2

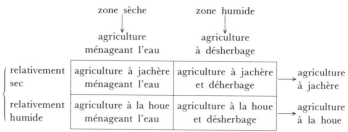

l'eau》). Là où l'indice annuel tombe au-dessous de 10, on se rapproche du type I.

Le type IV correspond aux régions les plus humides, à pluies d'été. Les mauvaises herbes y poussent dru l'été, mais en Europe septentrionale, relativement sèche, à températures plutôt basses et à sol pauvre, on pouvait dans le système traditionnel cultiver le blé et l'orge deux ans de suite, les champs étant laissés en jachère la troisième année. Un labour profond enfouissait l'herbe (《agriculture à jachère et désherbage》). Ce système a été pratiqué du Moyen Age jusqu'à une date assez récente.

Finalenent, l'Asie de l'Est et du Sud-Est représete la plus humide partie de la région humide. Les étés sont chauds et pluvieux, les mauvaises herbes poussent alors prolifiquement, et doivent, du printemps à l'automne, être souvent enlevées à la hous. Les mauvaises herbes et les insectes peuvent aisément ruiner les récoltes (《agriculture à la houe avec désherbage》).

Ainsi (tableau 2) peut-on diviser la céréaliculture traditionnelle en deux classes 《ménageant l'eau》 et 《à désherbage》, elles-mêmes subdivisées en deux sous-classes 《à jachère》 et 《à la houe》. Ces deux derniers types sont profondément différents : dans l'agriculture à jachère la productivité du sol peut être rétablie par le repos des champs ; il en va tout autrement dans la zone de la houe, une jachère y abaisserait la fertilité des sols — les substances organiques étant décomposées rapidement, et évacuées de même, lors des étés chauds et humides. D'autre part, dans l'agriculture à jachère, on ne bêche pas les champs, mais seulement les jardins, alors qu'on bêche champs et jardins dans l'autre zone — on ne peut donc y distinguer jardinage et agriculture.

Si le travail est intensif, la productivité du sol est supérieure dans l'agriculture à la hous. On peut y nourrir une vache avec l'herbe d'un champ de 10 ares[1] : cela semble impossible dans l'agriculture à jachère, même si le travail est très intensif. La limite inférieure du travail nécessaire est plus élevée dans l'agriculture à la hous ; et, si l'intensité du travail est au-dessous de cette limite, les résultats sont plus médiocres que dans l'agriculture à jachère ; en revanche, toute addition de travail au-desus de cette limite (intensification) donne des résultats meilleurs dans la culture à la houe. Autrement dit, celle-ci est bien plus sensible au degré d'intensité du travail.

On cherche à améliorer l'efficacité du travail, dans les deux cas, par l'emploi de machines et autres innovations ; mais l'affectation de la capacité de travail libérée par l'accroissement de productivité n'est pas la même. Dans l'agriculture à jachère, le travail économisé est utilisé pour agrandir l'exploitation ; dans la culture à la houe, il est réinvesti pour accroître encore l'intensité de la culture puisque, comme on l'a vu, les rendements sont bien plus sensibles à l'intensité du travail que dans l'agriculture à jachère. Ce ne sont évidemment là que des tendances générales : elles n'empêchent pas qu'il y ait une part d'intensification dans l'agriculture à jachère, une part d'agrandissement dans la culture à la houe.

II. L'ÉVOLUTION DE LA CULTURE CÉRÉALIÈRE DANS LE MONDE.

Les théories sur l'origine de l'agriculture sont nombreuses, mais l'interprétation d'E. Werth semble la plus raisonnable [2]. Werth pense en termes de «complexe

cultural⟩ et divise le monde en deux types, le complexe
inférieur à houe, le complexe supérieur à charrue. Dans
le premier, l'humanité a commencé à cultiver en zone
tropicale, uniquement des racines, avec des bâtons à fouir
et des houes primitives. Dans le second, la culture des
céréales a utilisé la charrue (du moins l'araire) dans son
cheminement de la zone tropicale à la zone tempérée —
moins favorable à l'agriculture. Werth estime que l'aire
d'origine du complexe à houe serait l'Asie du Sud-Est,
celle du complexe à araire l'Asie du Sud-Ouest.

De l'Asie du Sud-Ouest, la culture céréalière s'est diffusée vers l'ouest — avec le blé — et vers l'est — avec le
millet, mais celui-ci n'était sans doute pas seul. La diffusion du blé vers l'ouest s'est faite dans une zone sèche, et
sous forme de ⟨culture sèche⟩, sauf dans les quelques
endroits oú il était possible d'irriguer. L'indice d'aridité
estivale y est inférieur à 5 : seule la culture de céréales
d'hiver est possible. Aussi la rotation fut-elle de type
biennal : on n'ensemence le même champ qu'une fois tous
les deux ans, en travaillant la jachère entre temps. Ce
système fut étendu par les Romains jusqu'en Grande-Bre-
tagne et au Rhin ; mais ces territoires sont dans la zone
humide (indice annuel supérieur à 20) et les céréales de
printemps pouvaient y être cultivées (indice estival
supérieur à 5) : le système biennal à jachère fut adapté et
évolua vers le triennal (céréale d'hiver-céréale de
printempps-jachère), entre le VIIIe et le XIIIe siècle.
Comme l'indice d'aridité estival reste au dessous de 11, il
n'était généralement pas nécessaire de recourir au désherbage à la houe ; mais la jachère travaillée en troisième
année devenat nécessaire pour désherber ; il s'agit alors
de labours profonds, contrairement aux labours superficiels de la jachére en système biennal, qui visaient bien
moins le désherbage que la conservation de l'eau. C'est
là une différence essentielle, et qui explique la substiution
de la charrue à l'araire. On est passé ainsi du type ⟨à
jachère, ménageant l'eau⟩ (et à araire) au type ⟨à

jachère, et désherbage⟩ (et à charrue).

Cette évolution est bien connue des ruralistes européens. Mais l'agriculture à la houe a aussi changé. La première description de la culture du millet a pu être trouvée au Pendjab (1200 av. J.-C. ? d'après le *Rig-Vada*[3]) et en Chine du Nord (2000 ? -1122 av. J.-C. dynastie Yin), combinée dans les deux cas à celle du blé et de l'orge. On est dans la zone sèche $(i < 20)$ et les outils étaient du type de l'araire (type indien et type chinois) ; mais la sécheresse n'est pas de même nature qu'au Proche-Orient ou en Méditerranée : l'indice estival est supérieur à 5, la culture des céréales de printemps est possible hors irrigation, quoiqu'un houage pour la conservation de l'eau doive être souvent pratiqué en été. L'humidité hivernale étant comparable à celle des pays mediterranéens, une culture d'hiver est possible. Mais, si la culture du millet semble ainsi être allée des régions du type ⟨ménageant l'eau⟩ aux régions du type ⟨désherbant⟩, il semble en être à l'inverse pour le cas du riz.

L'aire originelle du riz est l'Asie du Sud-Est[4]. Sa culture s'est diffusée vers l'ouest et vers le nord, mais apparemment sans charrus : les outils étaient le bâton à fouir et la houe primitive, selon les données archéologiques et littéraires. La première culture du riz vient du complexe ⟨à houe⟩ et non du complexe ⟨à charrue⟩, et n'a aucun lien avec la culture sèche du Pendjab ou de la Chine du Nord, bien que Werth pense qu'elle proviendrat du complexe originel d'Asie occidentale, comme celle du blé.

La première trace archéologique du riz a été trouvée à Yangshao dans le Ho-nan (2200-1900 av. J.-C.) en Chine du Nord mais, selon la littérature, on ne trouve pas de culture du riz avant le VIIIe siècle av. J.-C. dans la vallée du Gange, ou le VIe siècle le long du Yangzi-jiang (Yang-tsé[5]). On peut inférer des annales du règne de Wu (Livres des Han, *Han-shu Wu-di Ji*, IIe siècle av. J.-

213

C.) et de la situation actuelle en Asie du Sud-Est, que la plus ancienne culture du riz en Asie humide était très extensive. Les mauvaises herbes étaint maîtrisées par une submersion pendant la période de croissance du riz, sans désherbage (《système à irrigation profonde constante》).

Dans la Chine du Nord et l'Inde septentrionale, selon le *Qimin Yaoshu* (VIᵉ siècle ap. J.-C.) et le Kṛṣi-parāśara (VIᵉ-VIIIᵉ siècle), un système de culture plus intensif était en oeuvre : on désherbait deux fois, et les champs étaient asséchés plusieurs fois [6] : c'était le 《système à drainage sporadique》. Il semble être une adaptation du système originel (à irrigation profonde constante) aux zones sèches. On ne connaît pas exactement la date de la transformation ; elle se situe entre la dynastie Tcheou (1122 av. J.-C.), qui marque le début de la culture du riz en Chine du Nord [7], et l'époque du *Qimin Yaoshu* (VIᵉ siècle ap. J.-C.), où l'on trouve la première description complète du nouveau système ; elle semble correspondre à la période des Royaumes combattants (403-221 av. J.-C.), pendant laquelle le génie hydraulique a fait de grands progrès en Chine du Nord.

L'application du système de drainage sporadique aux rizières dans la zone sèche a donc permis l'introduction d'uneforme de 《culture sèche》 — au sens de 《dry farming》 — en zone humide. Or celle-ci s'avérait plus productive que le système antérieur et, dès lors, a envahi en retour l'Asie humide, accompagnée des araires de zone sèche (indiens ou chinois [8]). Toutefois, elle n'a pas conquis l'Asie du Sud-Est, qui est restée fidèle au système à irrigation profonde constante, en raison de l'importance des aménagements anciens, des conditions climatiques et de l'emploi d'autres variétés de riz.

Il y a une grande différence entre le passage du système à ennoyage constant au système à assèchement sporadique en Asie humide, et le passage de l'assolement biennal au triennal en Europe humide. Dans le second cas, la charrue de zone humide a remplacé l'araire de zone sèche ; dans le premier, l'araire de zone séche n'a pas été remplacé, sauf au Japon depuis les XIXe et XXe siècles. La culture du riz, née en zone humide, n'a pas adopté un instrument propre à celle-ci ; tantôt on n'a pas utilisé de charrue ou d'araire du tout, même en système à assèchement sporadique (par exemple au Japon), tantôt on a employé l'araire de zone sèche dans le système à submersion constante, qui ne connaissait aucune forme de charre à l'origine (par exemple en Asie du Sud-Est).

Il existe de nombreuses théories sur l'introduction du riz au Japon ; mais on s'accorde à reconnaître depuis quelque temps qu'il aurait été introduit au IIIe siècle av. J.-C. à partir de la vallée du Yangzi-jiang[9]. S'il en est bien ainsi, elle l'a été sous la forme du système ancien (à irrigation profonde constante et sans araire) ; il n'y a effectivement aucune trace archéologique d'araire avant le Ve ou le VIe siècle ap. J.-C. and Japon[10]. Plus tard, le système à assèchement sporadique établi en Chine du Nord fut diffusé en Corée du Nord, dans des conditions climatiques similaires ; il ne fut introduit au Japon que par he Corée du Sud ; le fait que le vocabulaire de la culture du riz ne soit pas le même en Corée du Nord et en Corée du Sud semble bien indiquer une origine différente[11].

Des allusions au système à assèchement sporadique se trouvent dans la littérature japonaise du VIIIe siècleap. J.-C[12]. A partir de cette date, les Japonais l'ont adopté, avec l'araire chinois ; mais ils ont également utilisé la houe ou la bêche : au XVIIe at au XVIIIe siècle en particulier, on emploie surtout la houe, qui seule permet un labour profond, imossible avec l'araire chinois. A l'époque Meiji (1868-1912), quand le Japon commença à étudier les technologies agricoles européennes et américaines, le gouvernement créa des écoles d'agriculture et des stations expérimentales, et embaucha des chercheurs et des ingénieurs occidentaux. Quelques-uns, surtout Max Fesca (qui fut au Japon de 1882 à 1895), démontrèrent clairemen l'erreur qui consistait à utiliser l'araire de zone séche pour le Japon humide. Il recommanda l'adoption d'une charrue sans sep (un type de charrue de zone humide) qui était utilisée à cette époque dans la région de Fukuoka ; cette charrue as diffusa rapidement dans tout le Japon à l'époque Meiji. Elle accélérait le drainage des rizières, permettant un plus large usage des engrais, et autorisait le choix de nouvelles variétés de riz. Un système plus productif de culture du riz s'élabora ainsi à la fin du XIXe siècle, qu'on appela ⟨⟨l'agronomie de Fukuoka⟩⟩. Toutefois, il demandait plus d'adresse, parce que la profondeur du labour était irrégulière en raison de l'absence de sep : on inventa une charrue à sep court au début du XXe siècle[13]. Le succès de l'agronomie de Fukuoka marquait l'achèvement du passage de l'agriculture de zone sèche à l'agriculture de zone humide en Asie.

Le développement de l'agriculture à la houe est plus complexe que le développement de l'agriculture à jachère. Dans le premier, la culture du millet passa du type ⟨⟨zone sèche⟩⟩ au type ⟨⟨zone humide⟩⟩, mais la culture du riz se développa du type ⟨⟨zone humide⟩⟩ au type ⟨⟨zone sèche⟩⟩ pour se transformer en un nouveau type ⟨⟨zone humide⟩⟩. Cette évolution complexe est due à ce double mouvement des cultures du millet et du riz.

CONCLUSION.

On a vu que le développement historique des agricultures ⟨⟨à jachère⟩⟩et ⟨⟨à houe⟩⟩a été très différent. L'agriculture à jachère s'est orientée vers une utilisation extensive du travail (mécanisation) et vers de grandes unités d'exploitation ; elle a atteint son sommet dans l'agriculture des Etats-Unis. De son côté, l'agricuiture à la houe est allée vers une utilisation plus intensive du travail ; c'est au Japon qu'elle atteint son maximum d'intensité. Les systèmes japonais et nord-maéricain dépassent incontestablement les agricultures européenne et sudest-asiatique, chacun à sa manière, tant pour la production par hectare que par le degré de domination de l'environnement naturel.

De long temps, et, en tous cas, depuis le XVIIe siècle si l'on en juge d'après les traités de l'époque, l'agriculture japonaise a développé un type de culture mixte fondé sur le travail de la famille, parce que ce type était adapté à l'agriculture à la houe. Or, les politiques de 《modernisation》 adoptées depuis 1960 vont à l'encontre de cette tradition. Cette date marque le début de la forte croissance économique du Japon ; il fallait alors dégager des masses de main-d'oeuvre rapidement. La mécanisation d'exploitations dont la superficie moyenne se trouvait autour d'un hectare libèrerait certainement d'importantes réserves de travail, et cette tendance serait appuyée si l'on encourageait la monoculture. La communauté agricole a fourni en effet aux usines leur main-d'oeuvre permanente ; en outre, elle y a ajouté les travilleurs à temps partiel. Pour compenser la perte de travail ainsi subie par l'agriculture, les exploitants japonais ont massivement recouru aux machines et aux engrais chimiques, ajoutant ainsi aux profits des industriels. Car ce changement d'affectation de la main-d'oeuvre aboutissait aussi à accroître le coût et les prix des produits agricoles, et l'exportation des produits manufacturés, en échange d'importation de produits agicoles et de matièers premières.

Le gouvernement commença alors à encourager l'importation de produits agricoles — à l'exception du riz, dont la culture était surveillée par un système de contrôle de la production alimetaire. Il en est résulté que : 1) en 1992, l'autosuffisance japonaise en production agricole était tombée à 67%, et à 30% en ce qui concerne les céréales, 15% pour le ble, 5% pour le soja ; 2) mécanisation et monoculture sont devenues la règle. Mais, en janvier 1978, les exploitation agricoles exclusivement consacrées à l'agriculture n'étaient plus que 12% du total

217

RÉSUMÉ

des exploitations ; la majorité des personnes participant à la production agricole étaient des vieillards et des femmes. Les prix des produits agricoles sont très élevés par rapport aux prix mondiaux [14]. L'agriculture japonaise décline rapidement. C'est le résultat de la négation des méthodes de culture traditionnelles.

Notes

(1) Chuichi MATUOKA, 《A Study on balancing the Feed Ration throughout the Year on the Basis of Early Cut*》. *Bulletion of the National Institute of Agricultural Scienes*, Series H, n° 1, 3, 6, 9, 17, Tokyo, 1951-1955 [le signe*signifie que les articles cités sont en japonais].

(2) Emil WERTH, *Grabstock, Hacke und Pflug*, Ludwigsburg, 1954.

(3) Les cultures mentionnées dans le *Rig-Veda* sont l'orge les haricots, le melon, le sésame et le millet du Japon (IWAMOTO Yutaka, 《L'agriculture dans l'Inde ancienne*》, *Kodaishi Koza*, VII, 1962, p. 254-263). Les principales cultures apparaissant dans les vestiges de la dynatie Yin sont le millet d'Italie, le millet commun et l'orge. (Motonosuke AMANO, *Etudes sur l'histoire de l'agriculture chinoise**, Tokyo 1962, p. 3-88).

(4) Tadayo WATABE, *La route du riz**, Tokyo, 1977.

(5) AMANO, *op. cit.*, p. 95 - 99, 115 - 116. — Kenjiro ICHIKAWA, *Généalogie des techniques de la riziculture en Asie du Sud-Est**, Tokyo, 1961, p. 37-41. — IWAMOTO, *op cit.*, p. 256-258.

(6) Sachio KUMASHIRO, 《Les principes du 《dry-farming》, de l'empirisme ancien aux expériences modernes*》, *Special Bulletin of College of Agriculture of Utsunomiya University*, 1. — IWAMOTO, 《le Kṛṣi-parāśara, traié d'agronomie de l'Inde ancienne*》, *Kodai Bunka*,XVIII, 1966, Kyoto, p. 1-8.

(7) Il existe nombre de théories sur l'intrduction de la culture du riz en Chine du Nord, mais je pense que celle d'AMANO — la culture daterait de la dynastie Tcheou — est la plue raisonnable (*op. cit.*, p. 128-138).

(8) AMANO, *op. cit.*, p. 171-471. — B. NISHIYAMA, 《Le développement de la riziculture iriguée an Chine*》, *Nogyo Sogo Kenkyu*, III, 1959, Tokyo, p. 135-139. — K. NISHIMURA, *La riziculture en Inde**, Tokyo, 1962. — ID., Indian Council of Agricultural Research, *Rice in India*, New Delhi, 1960. — ID., *Rice Cultivation in India*, New Delhi, 1956.

(9) Je pense que la théorie d'Ando est la plus raisonnable (ANDO

218

RÉSUMÉ

Hirotaro, *Etudes sur la riziculture dans le Japon ancien**, Tokyo, 1959, p. 5-59). Toutefois, ANDO pense que la date d'introduction de la culture du riz au Japon est le IIe siècle av. J.-C.; ce serait plutô le IIIe siècle av. J.-C. d'après la Société Archéologique du Japon (*Origine et croissance de la communauté rurale au Japon**, Tokyo, Société Archéologique du Japon, I, 1961, p. 30-32).

(10) Akio OKAMOTO, 《Outils*》, *Nihon no Kokogaku*, III, 1961, p. 246.

(11) Shimpei OGURA, *Etudes de dilectologie coréenne**, Tokyo, 1944. S'appuyant sur ce livre, ANDO ne croit pas que la culture du riz ait pu être diffusée en Corée du Sud à partir de la Corée du Nord, puisque les dialectes concernant le riz sont très différents (*op. cit.*, p. 22). Toutefois, si un type de culture du riz a été diffusé en Corée du Sud à partir de la vallée du Yangzijiang et que, plusieurs siècles après, l'autre type de culture du riz a été diffusé de Chine du Nord en Corée du Nord, les différences de vocabulaire ne permettent pas d'inférer que cedernier type ne s'est pas diffusé ensute de Corée du Nord en Corée du Sud.

(12) Toshio FURUSHIMA, *Histoire de l'agriculture japonaise**, Tokyo I, 1947, I, p. 55-100. Mais Susumu YATSUGA affirme que les Système à drainage sporadique a été introduit au Japon à la fin du IVe siècle (YATSUGA S., 《Le développement des rizières dans le Japon ancien*》, *Nihonshi Kenkyu*, 96, 1966).

(13) IINUMA, 《The Effects of Industrialization of Agricultural Technology in Japon since 1800, especially after 1868 (*Meiji Restoration*)》, *Acta Museorum Agriculturae*, XI, 1, 1976, Prague, p. 100-104 ; ID., 《The Introduction of American and European Agricultural Science into Japan in the Meiji era》in R. T. SHAND, ed., *Technical Chang in Asian Agriculture*, Australian National University Press, Canberra, 1973, p. 1-8 ; et surtout ID., 《The Development of Japanese Plough in the First Half of the 20th Century》, in *Zinbun : Memoirs of the Research Institute for Humanistic Studies of Kyoto University*, Golden Jubileen Volume, 15, 1979, Kyoto.

(14) NORIN TOKEI KYOKAI ed., *Annuaire de la Statistique de l'agriculture japonaise 1992**. Tokyo, 1992.

BIBLIOGRAPHY

Amano, M. (1956) Shunju sengoku jidai no nogyo to sono shakai kozo.(Agriculture and Social Structure in the *Cn'un-ch'in* and *Chan-kuo* Period) in : Matsuyama shodai ronshu, Vol. 7, No. 3, Matsuyama.

Amano, M. (1962) Chugoku nogyoshi kenkyu. (Studies of Chinese Agricultural History), Tokyo.

Ando, H. (1959) Nihon kodai inasakushi kenkyu. (A Study of Rice Cultivation in Ancient Japan) Tokyo.

Ando, Y. ed. (1975) Kindai nihon keizaishi yoran. (Manual of Japanese Economic History), Tokyo.

Arimitsu, K. (1967) Chosen sangoku jidai no nogu to kogu. (Tools of the Three Kingdom Period of Korea) in : Nihon no kokogaku (Japanese Archaeology) Vol. 6, Tokyo.

Asahi shimbunsha ed., (1930) Nihon keizai tokei sokan. (The Complete Economic Statistics of Japan), Tokyo.

Azuma, U., (1979) Chosen sangoku jidai no noko. (Agriculture in the Three Kingdum Period of Korea) in : Kashiwara kokogaku kenkyujo ronshu, Vol. 4, Nara.

British Museum, An Illustration in the 14th Century of Luttrell Psalter.

Cambridge Economic History of Europe, (1941) Vol. 1, London.

Chosen sotokufu ed., (1916) Chosen koseki zufu. (Japanese Government-General of Korea ed., Catalogue of Historical Remains of Korea), Vol. 3, Keijo.

Chosen sotokufu ed., (1924) Chosen no zairai nogu. (The Traditional Agricultural Implements of Korea), Keijo.

Chosen sotokufued., (1937) Beikoku yoran (Statistics of Rice in Korea), Keiyo.

Chugoku kagakuin koko kenkyujo ed., (1956) Kiken hokkutsu hoko-ku (Institute of Archaeology of the Academy of Sciences of China ed., A Report on the Excavation in *Huixian*) Peiping.

Dainainihon nokai ed., (1881) Dainohon nokaiho. (Report of the Agricultural Science Society of Japan), Tokyo.

Elton, G. R., (1953) The Tuder Revolution in Government, London.

Fesca, M. (1888) Nogyo kairyo an. (A Plan for Improving Japanese Agriculture) in : Meiji zenki kanno jiseki shuroku (Collection of Materials for the Encouragement of Agricultural Production by

Japanese Government in the First Half of Meiji Era), Vol. 2, Tokyo, 1939.

Fesca, M. (1891) Nihon chisan ron, tokuhen. (Beiträge zur Kenntniss der Japanischen Landwirtschaft, Allgemeiner Theil 1890 – Spezieller Theil 1893), Tokyo.

Franklin, T. B. (1919) A History of Agriculture, London.

Fukuda, T., (1900) Die gesellschaftliche und wirtschatliche Entwickelung in Japan, Stuttgart.

Fukuokaken ed., (1879) Nomushi Gyogyoshi. (Survey of Agricultural and Fishing Implements in Fukuoka Prefecture), Fukuoka; rep. Fukuoka, 1982.

Furushima, T. (1949) Nihon nogyo gijyusushi (The History of Japanese Agricultural Technology), Vol. 2, Tokyo.

Government of the Republic of Korea ed., (1969) Agricultural Implements, Seoul.

Gras, N. S. B., (1925) A History of Agriculture in Europe and America, N. Y.

Hatakeyama, H. (1964) Ajiya no kiko. (Climate in Asia), Tokyo.

Heibonsha ed., (1966) Hyakkaziten. (Encyclopedia), Vol. 11, Tokyo.

Huang, Zhan-yue, (1957) Iron Tools unearthed recently in the *Chan-kuo* and *Han* Priod, in : Koko gakuho (Bulletin of Archaeology), Vol. 3, Peiping : cited in Amano, Chugoku nogyo kenkyu.

Iinuma, J., (1969a) Meiji zenki no nogyo kyoiku. (Agricultural Education in the First Half of the Meiji Era), Kyoto.

Iinuma, J. (1969b) The Meiji System : the Revolution of Rice Cultivation Technology in Japan, in : Agricultural History, Vol. 43, No. 2 : pp. 289-96.

Iinuma, J. (1969c) The ne-no-hi-kara-suki of shosoin, in : Tools and Tillage, Vol. 1, No. 2.

Ikata, S., (1941) Nihon kodai no mugi ni tsuite. (Study on Wheat and Barley of Ancient Japan) in : Nogyo keizai kenkyu, Vol. 17, No. 4, Tokyo.

Ikata, S., (1945) Nihon kodai kachikushi. (History of Cattles of Ancient Japan), Tokyo.

Ishida, E., (1968) Shimpojumu : Nihon noko bunka no kigen. (Symposium on the Origin of Agriculture in Japan), Tokyo.

Iwata, K., (1966) Nihon Bunka no Furusato (The native place of Japanese Culture) Tokyo.

Johson, H., (1909) The Disapperance of the Small Landowner, London.

Kindleberger, C. P., (1964) Economic Growth in France and Britain 1851-1950, London.

Kinoshita, T., (1966) Nogu. (Farming Tools) in : Nihon no kokoga-

221

ku (Japanese Archaeology) Vol. 3, Tokyo.

Kinoshita, T., (1979) kodai no suki. (Plough in Ancient Japan) in : Dainihon nokai ed., Nihon no kama kuwa suki. (Japanese Sickles, Hoes and Ploughs), Tokyo.

Kishida, Y., (1954) Matsuyama genzo o hyoden. (A Life of Genzo Matsuyama), Tokyo.

Kuczinski, J., (1967) Die Geschichte der Lage der Arbeit unter den Kapitalismus, Bd. 37, Berlin.

Liu, Hsien-chou, (1963) History of Invention of Agricultural Implements of Ancient China, Peiping.

Martonne, E. de., (1942) Nouvell carte mondiale de l'indice d'aridite, in : Annales de Géographie, tome LI, Paris.

Miyata, N., (1970) Ikigami shinko (Faith of Living Deities), Tokyo.

Miyazaki, Y., (1967) Nogyo zensho. (Complete Book of Farming), Kyoto.

Nef, J. U., (1940) Industry and Government in France and England, 1540-1640, London.

Nihon kokogakkai ed., (1961) Nihon noko bunka no seisei. (Japan Archaeological Society ed., The Origin and Growth of Farming Community in Japan), Vol. 1, Tokyo.

Nishimura, T., (1966) Indo momen kogyoshi. (History of the Indian Cotton Industry), Tokyo.

Norinsho nettai nogyo kenkyu senta ed., (1976) Kyu chosen ni okeru nihon no nogyo shiken no seika. (Research Centre of the Tropical Agriculture of the Department and Forestry of Japanese Government ed., Results of Agricultural Experiments and Researches by Japanese Scholars in the Colonial Korea), Tokyo.

Noshomusho ed., (1881) Meiji 14 nen zenkoku nodankai nissi. (The Deparrtment of Agriculture and Commerce of Japanese Government ed., A Report of All Japan Agricultural Conference), Tokyo. cited in : Nihon nogyo hattatsushi (History of Agriculture since the Meiji Era), Vol. 1, Tokyo, 1953.

Noshomusho ed., (1905) Kankoku tochi nosan chosa hokoku. (The Department of Agriculture and Commerce of Japanese Government ed., Reports of Agricultural Surveys in Korea), Tokyo.

Nunokawa, & Sakane, T. ed., (1967) Takakita shinjiro. (A Life of Shinjiro Takakita) in : Hatsumei no gijutsu (The Technology of Invention), Tokyo.

Okamoto, A., (1966) Nogyo seisan. (Agricultural Production) in : Nihon no kokogaku (Japanese Archaeology) Vol. 5, Tokyo.

Orwin, C. S., (1949) A History of English Farming, London.

Orwin, C. S. & C. S., (1938) The Open Fields, London.

Ouchi, H., (1946) Zaiseigaku taiko. (The Science of Finance), Vol. 2, Tokyo.

Saegusa, H. & others, (1960) Kindai nihon sangyo gijutsu no seioka. (Westerization of the Industrial and Agricultural Technology since the Meiji Era), Tokyo.

Saito, Y., (1968) Nihon nogakushi. (A History of Japanese Agricultural Sciences), Tokyo.

Sakaideshi ed., (1985) The Excavated Data of a Historical Site at Shimokawatsu, Sakaide.

Sekino, T., (1959) Sin raishi ko. (New Researches on the Lei-su) in : Tokyo Unibunka kiyo (The Memoirs of the Insitute for Oriental Culture of Tokyo University), Vol. 19, Tokyo.

Simizu, H., (1953) Gyubako no Fukyu to Koungijutsu no Hattatsu (Diffusion of Ploughing by Cattles and Development of Farming Tochnology) in : Nogyo Hattatsushi Chosakai ed., Nihon Nogyo Hattatsushi (The History of Japanese Agriculture) Vol. 1, Tokyo.

Simizu, H., (1979) Wari no keisei to yakuwari. (Roles and Formation of Japanese Ploughs) in : Dainihon nokai ed., Nihon no kama kuwa suki (Japanese Hoes, Sickles and Ploughs) Tokyo.

Suzuki, S., (1960) Hyuga no tekki. (Iron Tools of Hyuga) in : Kodaigaku kenkyu, Vol. 25, Tokyo.

Tanaka, S., (1941) Waga kuni no suki no kigen oyobi meiji ishin madeno hattatsu no keiro ni tsuite. (Origin and History of the Plough in Japan until the Meiji Restoration) in : Nogyo kikaigakkaishi, Vol. 5, No. 3, Tokyo.

Taniura, Y., (1966) Kankoku no nogyo to tochiseido. (Agriculture and Land System in Korea), Tokyo.

Teishitsu hakubutsukan ed., (1942) Shosoin gyobutsu zuroku. (The Imperial Household Museum ed., Catalogue of Treasures in the Imperial Treasures of Shosoin), Vol. 14, Tokyo.

Tsude, H., (1967) Nogu tekkika no futatsu no kakki. (Two Epochs in the Process of the Change from Wooden Farming Tools to Iron Ones) in : Kokogaku kenkyu, Vol. 13, No. 3 ,Tokyo.

Tsukuba, T., (1959) Nihon nogyo gijutsushi. (The History of Japanese Agricultural Technology), Tokyo.

Tull, J., (1733) The Horse Hoeing Husbandry, London.

Ueda, M., (1965) Kikajin. (Naturalized Persons in Ancient Japan), Tokyo.

Ueda, M., (1970) Nihon Shinwa (Japanese Mythology,) Tokyo.

Wang, Chen. The Book of Agriculture. (original edition from the Yüan Period).

Werth, E., (1954) Grabstock, Hacke und Pflug, Ludwigsburg.

Widtsoe, J. A., (1919) Dry Farming, N. Y.

Yanaihara, T., (1936) Teikokushuki ka no indo. (India under Imperialism) in ; Yanaihara Tadao zensho (Complete Works of T. Yanaihara), Vol. 3, Tokyo, 1963.

223

Yasuda, S. ed., (1952) Meiji iko ni okeru nogyo gijutsu no hattatsu. (The Development of Agricultural Technology since the Meiji Era), Tokyo.
Yomiuri shinbunsha ed., (1979) Chuka jinmin kyowakoku shiruku rodo bunbutsu ten. (A Book of the Exhibition of Ancient Art Treasures of the People's Republic of China : Archaeological Finds of the *Han* to *Tang* Dynasty unearthed at Sites along the Silk Road), Tokyo.

Japanese Farming : Past and Present

1995 年 9 月 24 日　第 1 刷発行

著　者　Jiro Iinuma

発行所　社団法人　農山漁村文化協会
郵便番号　107　東京都港区赤坂 7 丁目 6 - 1
電話 東京(3585)1141(代)振替00120=3=　144478

ISBN4 - 540 - 95014 - 2 C3061 P3,000E
ⓒ 1995 Jiro Iinuma
Printed in Japan　印刷・製本／共同印刷工業(株)